SD ▌K228 The science of the mind:
inv ◖stigating mental health
Sci ◖ence: Level 2

The Open University

Book 4
Dementias

This publication forms part of the Open University module SDK228 *The science of the mind: investigating mental health*. Details of this and other Open University modules can be obtained from the Student Registration and Enquiry Service, The Open University, PO Box 197, Milton Keynes MK7 6BJ, United Kingdom (tel. +44 (0)845 300 60 90; email general-enquiries@open.ac.uk).

Alternatively, you may visit the Open University website at www.open.ac.uk where you can learn more about the wide range of modules and packs offered at all levels by The Open University.

To purchase a selection of Open University materials visit www.ouw.co.uk, or contact Open University Worldwide, Walton Hall, Milton Keynes MK7 6AA, United Kingdom for a brochure (tel. +44 (0)1908 858793; fax +44 (0)1908 858787; email ouw-customer-services@open.ac.uk).

The Open University, Walton Hall, Milton Keynes MK7 6AA

First published 2011

Edited and designed by The Open University.

Typeset by The Open University

Printed and bound in Malta by Progress Press Co. Ltd.

ISBN 978 1 8487 3548 4

1.1

The paper used in this publication is procured from forests independently certified to the level of Forest Stewardship Council (FSC) principles and criteria. Chain of custody certification allows the tracing of this paper back to specific forest-management units (see www.fsc.org).

Contents

Chapter 3 Pharmacological approaches to the treatment of Alzheimer's

Katherine Leys, Claire Rostron and Christine Heading

Chapter 1 The experience and diagnosis of dementia

Antonio Martins-Mourao

1.1 Introducing dementia: a mental health challenge for the 21st century

You have reached the last book in SDK228, which will be dedicated to the **dementias**. In Chapter 1 you will be introduced to the main types of dementia (Alzheimer's dementia, frontotemporal dementia and vascular dementia) and the signs and symptoms associated with these, exploring how they are assessed and diagnosed. Chapter 2 then presents essential information about the biology of Alzheimer's dementia to explain how neuron death happens in the brain. Chapter 3 continues the focus on Alzheimer's dementia, and will look at the current drug treatments available for this condition and the search to find more effective therapies. Chapter 4 will broaden the focus again to all forms of dementia, reviewing psychosocial therapies and evaluating their strengths and limitations. Chapter 4 also discusses perspectives in dementia and the impact that these perspectives have on treatment and care.

The term 'dementia' derives from the Latin *de* (out of) and *mens* (mind), meaning 'out of one's mind'.

1.2 Understanding dementia

Dementia can be understood as a disorder of the brain, because it is linked to neurodegeneration and widespread changes in brain function (Henderson and Jorm, 2002). There is deterioration in the way individuals think, feel and communicate. This can be illustrated with the case of Martha, aged 76, who is a respected academic known for her work in the field of genetics (Figure 1.1). Her son's description of his mother, now diagnosed with dementia (Vignette 1.1), does not resemble the professor everyone remembers. It does, however, illustrate the dramatic changes that can be brought about by neurodegeneration in dementia cases.

Neurodegeneration (or neuronal degeneration) refers to the progressive death of neurons in the brain.

Figure 1.1 Martha has been diagnosed with dementia.

Vignette 1.1 Experiences of dementia: Martha and Saul

Saul describes his mother, Martha:

> I hadn't seen my mother for about three months and nothing could prepare me for the changes I saw that afternoon when I visited the home where she now stays. As she walked into the garden my sister said something nice like, 'look, Mom, look who is here dying to give you a kiss!', but I felt right away that she no longer recognised me. She looked confused and then said, 'Hello young man, I'm sorry but I no longer teach …'. She then turned to Sandra (my sister) and asked for a glass of water. As Sandra went for the water I noticed that my mother began to follow her back into the house, so I pointed at some seats nearby and said, 'Mom would you like to sit down?' I immediately got this terrible feeling that she didn't want to be left alone with me because she thought I was a stranger. She turned to me and she said, 'Who are you? Didn't see you there … Can you get me a taxi? This nurse here is nasty … all she wants is my money'. My mother was referring to my sister. She had mistaken her for a nurse. It was just heartbreaking.

Dementia is a progressive condition. This means that, as the dementia advances, nearly all brain functions, including memory, language, judgement and the emotions, are affected. As memory problems worsen, individuals begin to have difficulty performing daily activities such as managing a bank account, and remembering to take their medications. People with dementia are often unable to focus attention on a conversation. They may lose the ability to recognise family members and to speak; or may suffer delusions such as the idea that their spouse is being unfaithful. Martha (Vignette 1.1) cannot recognise her son or her daughter and is worried that the 'nurse' will steal from her.

As neuronal death spreads, the condition also affects the person's emotions and social behaviour. They may become aggressive, agitated and depressive or have difficulties sleeping. Others may become irritable and hostile. They may also become disoriented about places and time.

During the late stages of dementia, individuals lose their ability to control motor functions: they may have difficulties swallowing, or lose bowel and bladder control, requiring, for these reasons, full-time care. Note that the progression of dementia varies from individual to individual. Inevitably, however, any differences that could be initially found between the various forms of dementia will later become blurred as the condition reaches its final stage.

This chapter will introduce you to the main types of dementia and will be looking at the prevalence and incidence of dementia. You will also explore the experience of not having memory, and we will briefly review the different types of memory and their location in the brain. The chapter will then concentrate on the various steps involved in the diagnosis of Alzheimer's dementia; in particular, highlighting the use of screening tools and questionnaires for the functional diagnosis of this condition. We will also distinguish between normal age-related memory decline and dementia, clarifying what is meant by mild cognitive impairment (MCI), a controversial term that defines a possible intermediary state between good mental health and dementia. Finally, we will be exploring the signs and symptoms, progression and prognosis of frontotemporal and vascular dementia.

1.2.1 Types of dementia

Dementia has probably affected humans ever since we began to survive in appreciable numbers into old age. However, in the UK, the condition has become much more noticeable in the last 30 years or so, because more people are now reaching old age. Whereas in the early 1980s men and women were expected to live to the ages of 71 and 77, respectively, at the time of writing (2010) they are expected to reach the ages of 77 and 82. These data, reported by the UK Office for National Statistics (2010), refer to the average life expectancy at birth.

The most common type of dementia is **Alzheimer's dementia** (AD), affecting about two-thirds of people with dementia. AD usually starts slowly so that it may be difficult to pinpoint the moment when the dementia manifested initially, as illustrated by Anna's recollections of her husband's initial symptoms (Vignette 1.2). Filip is a retired GP.

Figure 1.2 Alois Alzheimer, who first described the pathology of a dementia case in 1906.

Vignette 1.2 Experiences of dementia: Filip and Anna

I'd noticed changes in Filip, my husband, two or three years before he was diagnosed, but it's so hard to pinpoint because Alzheimer's begins so subtly. There are little changes here and there but it's also very difficult to face a situation where you suspect your partner of a lifetime may have such a terrible illness. On one occasion, my sister brought a friend home, and Filip began chatting with her. Fifteen minutes later, I think we all noticed that he repeated exactly the same questions. Later, my sister said to me, 'Did you hear Filip? Do you think he's developing Alzheimer's?' This was the first proper mention of the word and it took the presence of someone outside our marriage to say it out loud. I just couldn't.

This form of dementia was named after the German psychiatrist and neuropathologist Alois Alzheimer (Figure 1.2), who described the condition in a 51-year-old woman, Auguste Deter (Figure 1.3), and performed a post-mortem examination of her brain upon her death in 1906. He was the first person to describe the brain **pathology**, or changes in structure of the brain, associated with a form of dementia.

The first symptoms of Alzheimer's dementia are often mild memory difficulties and mild confusion that may be seen, for example, when the person has difficulties managing bills or when they get lost on their way home. But what happens in the brain to cause these changes? Brains affected

Figure 1.3 Auguste Deter, who was diagnosed with a form of dementia later known as Alzheimer's dementia.

by AD produce two types of abnormal deposits. The first leads to the formation of clumps called *plaques*, whilst the second changes the structure of neurons to the point of forcing them to collapse on themselves, creating clumps called *tangles*. Such structural changes disable communications between neurons and, as a result, the person is no longer able to function normally. You will learn more about the biology of Alzheimer's dementia in Chapter 2 of this book.

Another type of dementia is **frontotemporal dementia**, affecting about one in 50 people with dementia. The term 'frontotemporal' refers to the frontal and temporal lobes in the brain because these are the main brain areas affected. This type of dementia is usually the most difficult to spot because it affects people in their fifties, when dementia is rarely suspected. Changes to the frontal lobes cause changes in personality, motivation and management of the emotions, typically resulting in unexpected aggressiveness. Disinhibited behaviour is also characteristic of frontotemporal dementia, as illustrated by Morag's story (Vignette 1.3a).

A third common type of dementia is **vascular dementia**, or multi-infarct dementia. The term **vascular** refers to the blood vessels of the brain. Around one in four people with dementia will have vascular dementia due to poor or interrupted blood (and hence oxygen) supply to the brain. As you will see in Section 1.6, the specific symptoms of vascular dementia will vary according to the areas of the brain that are affected, but Joy's story illustrates symptoms that are common to many people with this type of dementia (Vignette 1.3b).

We will return to each of these three types of dementia in Sections 1.4, 1.5 and 1.6 of this chapter.

Vignette 1.3 Frontotemporal and vascular dementias

(a) Frontemporal dementia: Morag and Jack

My name is Jack and my sister Morag has been diagnosed with frontotemporal dementia. She is 57 years old. One day she didn't turn up for a visit we had planned, and when I went to her home I discovered that she had started hoarding. I had not been inside her house in several years because whenever I went there she would meet me outside and would not invite me in. I didn't think anything of it at the time. I found Morag lying on her bed in filthy clothes. There were no sheets or blankets on the bed, and she was just lying in her own urine but she didn't seem a bit bothered. She was living in a complete mess, surrounded by litter and boxes and packages of stuff that she had bought from TV shopping channels and never opened. My sister absolutely hated the visit and could not see what 'all the fuss was about'.

(b) Vascular dementia: Joy and Chantelle

Shortly after her 79th birthday my mother, Joy, started to show behavioural changes and some memory loss and confusion. We just thought it was old age catching up with her. But she started wandering and she could become quite violent. She would also see imaginary people – she said there were boys hiding in her wardrobe, and that some woman was stealing her clothes. She would shout at them and sometimes throw things too. She lived with us for a while but it became obvious that she couldn't be left alone for very long so I had to leave my job to look after her.

Primary and secondary dementias

Dementias can also be classified as primary or secondary. **Primary dementias** such as the ones described above are those that do not result from any other physiological condition. **Secondary dementias**, on the other hand, may occur as a result of brain trauma, infectious diseases, metabolic disorders, vitamin deficiencies or other underlying medical conditions. Some ex-professional boxers, for example, may develop dementia that is secondary to the various injuries sustained in the head during their careers.

An essential aspect of all forms of dementia is that, due to neuronal death, the person will progressively lose awareness of their environment. They will also lose control over their actions. We turn to this issue in the next section.

1.2.2 Loss of awareness and control

Dementia changes the personalities, capacities and habits of people who, consequently, may become strangers to family members and friends. This has happened in Martha's case (Vignette 1.1), for example. However, none of these dramatic changes will be under her conscious control. Martha is simply not aware that she is mistaking her daughter for a nurse she also suspects is stealing from her.

As such, the typical lack of cooperation and apparent abandonment that characterises people with dementia should not be attributed to aggressiveness, laziness or having 'let go'. Instead, the variations observed in the behaviour and attitude of people with dementia will, in the majority of cases, bear a direct relation to the specific areas of the brain being affected, which vary considerably from one individual to the next.

■   What biological changes can be linked to the dramatic changes often observed in people with dementia?

□   Progressive neurodegeneration.

However, although it is clear that progressive neurodegeneration occurs in dementia, little is known about why individuals develop dementia in the first place. Its onset could be influenced by a range of biological, social and environmental factors such as genetics and lifestyle. In order to investigate the various influences on the onset of dementia, researchers have focused on risk factors, which we turn to in the next section.

1.2.3 Risk factors for dementia

Note that being at risk of developing a disorder does not necessarily mean that a person will develop it. Being at risk merely means that the chance of developing the disorder is increased. For example, by smoking cigarettes people may increase their chances of developing lung cancer.

Age as a risk factor

The greatest risk factor associated with dementia is age, which means that the chance of an individual developing dementia increases as they get older. However, as you will see, this does not mean that developing dementia is a certainty.

■   What does the statement 'one in 20 people over 65 has dementia' mean?

To plan for his future, a middle-aged man might want to know his chances of having dementia at the age of 85: for this he needs prevalence data. By contrast, a fit 82-year-old man might want to know his chances of developing dementia before he is 85: for this, he needs the incidence data.

□   The statement means that *prevalence* of dementia within the whole population aged 65 years and above is 5%.

■   Can you define prevalence and incidence?

□   Prevalence, you may remember from Book 1, Section 4.2.5, refers to the number of people with the condition at a particular time; incidence refers to the number of people developing the condition within a particular timeframe, usually 12 months.

Scientists use prevalence surveys to estimate the proportion of individuals within a defined population (country or region) that have a health condition at a particular point in time, thereby allowing health organisations and governments to plan adequate services. Whilst prevalence data are essential for those planning for health care provision, prevalence and incidence data allow epidemiologists to develop and test theories about possible risk factors for dementia. Such studies collect information about age, gender and geographical location, which will be useful to investigate their role as risk factors for dementia.

Table 1.1 shows the results of the EURODEM study, one of the most recent meta-analyses (Book 2, Box 1.7) of European population-based surveys carried out in the 1990s, using data from 11 studies that took place in eight European countries (Lobo et al., 2000). On the right-hand side are the estimated prevalence data for late onset dementia (this refers to all forms of dementia diagnosed after the age of 65). The values are expressed as the percentage of individuals in a particular age group that suffer from dementia. Note that there were no important differences in the age-specific prevalence between studies or between countries, so the data are valid for all European countries in the study, including the UK.

Table 1.1 allows some useful comparisons between prevalence and incidence rates for dementia. So, for example, whilst the prevalence data suggest that 5.8% of individuals aged 75–79 will have late onset dementia, the incidence data (on the left-hand side) indicate that for someone aged 75 who is dementia-free, there is only a 1.6% chance of developing dementia in the following year.

Table 1.1 Incidence and prevalence rates of dementia from the EURODEM meta-analysis of European studies.

Age group	Annual incidence (%)			Prevalence (%)		
	Males	Females	Average	Males	Females	Average
65–69	0.2	0.3	0.3	1.6	1.0	1.3
70–74	0.6	0.5	0.6	2.9	3.1	3.0
75–79	1.4	1.8	1.6	5.6	6.0	5.8
80–84	2.8	3.4	3.1	11.0	12.6	11.8
85–89	3.9	5.4	4.7	12.8	20.2	16.5
90+	4.0	8.2	6.1	22.1	30.8	26.5

As you can see, incidence data can be useful when reassuring older individuals who are worried about their chances of developing the condition. We will return to this issue in Section 1.4.6 dedicated to mild cognitive impairment, where researchers investigate the percentages of individuals that may develop dementia within a limited number of months.

■ How *meaningful* is the statement 'one in 20 people over 65 has dementia?'

☐ Although the statement means that within the whole population aged 65 and over the prevalence is 5%, this percentage varies considerably according to age group. For example, prevalence for people aged 65–69 is just over 1%; but for those aged 80–84 it is nearly 12%. So the indication of a specific age group is essential to ensure accuracy.

It is worth noting here that neither the incidence nor prevalence data we have discussed include early onset dementia. Early onset dementia is a term that covers a range of conditions affecting memory, thinking and emotional management in people under the age of 65. This is a relatively rare condition, thought to account for about 2.2% of UK dementia cases, and is composed mostly of cases of frontotemporal dementia. A rare form of Alzheimer's dementia affecting people under 65 is discussed in Chapter 2.

Gender as a risk factor

Table 1.1 also shows the percentages of both women and men in each age group with late onset dementia. This information will help you to clarify whether one gender is more likely to develop dementia than the other. As you can see, there seems to be a slight variation in prevalence and incidence between genders at some ages. Despite this, however, there is widespread agreement that gender is not a strong biological risk factor for dementia.

Geographical region as a risk factor

Finally, although the EURODEM study showed that prevalence rates did not vary *within* a region (in this case, Europe), other evidence shows that prevalence rates for dementia may vary *between* regions (Table 1.2), which suggests that geographical location may be a risk factor for dementia. For example, countries in Western Europe, North and South America and the Middle East have higher prevalence rates for dementia in comparison with Sub-Saharan Africa and India and neighbouring countries (Ferri et al., 2005). The incidence rates in the Sub-Saharan region and India are also much lower than those reported in developed countries (Hendrie et al., 2001; Chandra et al., 2001).

Whether these differences may be explained by cultural aspects, such as type of family support, lifestyle or differences in diagnostic practices, remains unclear (mild dementia is ignored in developing countries because of cultural differences, for example). Another possibility is that the assessment criteria used in some developing countries such as India or Nigeria, for example, may not be adapted to non-Western populations.

Table 1.2 Alzheimer's Disease International (2008) consensus estimates for the prevalence of dementia (%), by WHO region and age group. The letters in the left-hand column refer to the level of development of a region; A = lowest mortality regions and D = highest mortality regions.

Level of development	Geographical region	65–69	70–74	75–79	80–84	85+
A	Western Europe	1.5	3.6	6.0	12.2	24.8
A	North America	1.7	3.3	6.5	12.8	30.1
B	China and neighbours	1.7	3.7	7.0	14.4	26.2
D	South America	1.7	3.4	7.6	14.8	33.2
D	North Africa, Middle East	1.9	3.9	6.6	13.9	23.5
D	India and neighbours	0.9	1.8	3.7	7.2	14.4
D	Sub-Saharan Africa	0.6	1.3	2.3	4.3	9.7

Activity 1.1 Analysing prevalence data
(LO 1.1) Allow 10 minutes

Take a look at the data in Table 1.2. Can the lower rates of dementia found in Sub-Saharan countries (final row) be explained by the level of development of the region? Does high mortality (i.e. the fact that very few people survive to 65 years of age) explain the lower rates in Sub-Saharan countries?

Considering that the majority of cases of Alzheimer's dementia typically begin with memory difficulties, we will next explore what memory loss may actually feel like. Also, to help you understand how memories are organised (or believed to be organised), and which parts of the brain seem to play a significant role in memorisation, we now turn to one of neuroscience's famous cases, Henry Molaison, who lost his ability to learn new facts before the age of 30.

1.3 The feeling of not having memory

Henry Molaison (Figure 1.4) was born in 1926. When he was nine, Henry, or HM, was hit by a cyclist and banged his head hard on the ground. Following this, HM soon began to experience minor epileptic episodes that later turned into frequent and uncontrollable seizures disabling him from earning a living. Uncontrollable seizures are those that do not respond to medication or any other form of medical treatment.

'Epilepsy' refers to a tendency to have recurrent seizures (sometimes called fits). A seizure is caused by a sudden burst of excess electrical activity in the brain, causing a temporary disruption in the normal communication between neurons.

Figure 1.4 Henry Molaison who 'lost his memory' at the age of 27.

When HM was 27, a brain surgeon, William Scoville, attempted to reduce the seizures by removing two finger-shaped slivers of tissue from HM's temporal lobes (Figure 1.5).

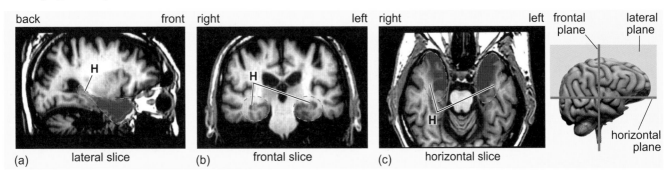

(a) lateral slice (b) frontal slice (c) horizontal slice

Figure 1.5 MRI scans of HM's medial temporal lobes obtained in 1998, aged 72. (a) Lateral, (b) frontal and (c) horizontal views. The areas defined by the dotted lines include the hippocampus (marked H) and adjacent cortical areas. Within these areas the darker regions indicate where tissue was removed by surgery.

The images show that the surgical removal was symmetrical and included most of the **hippocampus** (marked H), an area deep in the brain, about level with the ears. The surgeon also removed some of the surrounding cortex in the medial temporal lobes. This is where the medical team had located the initial source of the epileptic fits using electroencephalography, or EEG, to which you were introduced in Book 1, Chapter 2.

'Medial temporal lobe' refers to the parts of the temporal lobe towards the centre of the brain.

1.3.1 Anterograde and retrograde amnesia

HM's operation was judged to be a success because the removal of the brain tissue reduced the number and severity of his seizures. However, *after* the procedure, HM began to show great difficulty in forming new memories or learning new facts. This form of memory impairment is known as **anterograde amnesia**. It is the inability to form new memories after a relevant incident such as an accident or surgery. Also, HM had incomplete memories for the events in the weeks before the operation, a phenomenon called **retrograde amnesia**: for example, he had no recall of the conversations with his surgeon leading up to the operation. As you will see, these impairments go some way towards illustrating what most people with Alzheimer's dementia experience every day.

It later emerged that HM could 'remember' something as long as he repeated it in his mind. But the information would vanish soon after he stopped the repetition. For instance, he could remember the number 584 for 15 minutes by continual rehearsal and using an elaborate **mnemonic scheme** – provided he was not distracted.

A mnemonic scheme is any special strategy that may be used to help remember something.

Also, despite his amnesia, HM could still learn new *skills* and he was able to negotiate a nearly normal day attending to mundane details. For example, he could prepare lunch, clean his bedroom, help with the shopping, mow the lawn and ride a bicycle. And when it came to socialising, he simply drew on what he could remember from the first 27 years of his life. HM lived to the age of 82 and died in December 2008.

So, why could HM learn and remember some things (motor skills, for example) but not others (such as what he had had for breakfast that morning)? It is precisely the investigation of this question that has made HM one of the most famous cases in neuroscience, as he single-handedly taught scientists a lot of what is currently known about the memorisation process and how memories may be organised in the brain. HM is therefore a very good example of how powerful a case study (Book 1, Box 4.11) can be. However, the surgeon William Scoville never performed the operation again, and in fact campaigned against it.

1.3.2 Memory subtypes and the role of the hippocampus

Crucially, HM's case showed that the hippocampus and adjacent temporal cortical areas play an essential role in the process of memorisation. Without them, he could no longer consolidate specific types of information in his memory. He could, however, retrieve information that had been encoded and consolidated prior to the surgery. **Encoding** is the process by which information or perceived events are transformed into a memory representation. **Consolidation**, on the other hand, is the process that fixes the information so that it becomes stable over time. Finally, **retrieval** refers to the process of accessing previously stored information.

However, the evidence from HM's case also suggested that memory is not a single or unitary system within the brain, and although the hippocampus and temporal cortex seem to be clearly being involved in some types of memory, they are not involved in others, as we shall now explore.

Working memory: the scratchpad

Working memory acts as a sort of scratchpad to record (or encode) temporary information that you may have in process. However, working memory is limited in size (how much you can keep in mind at any one time) and fades away quickly if not actively rehearsed (reciting a phone number to ring for a taxi, for example). This explains why HM needed to repeat the contents of his working memory over and over again to avoid forgetting them. Unlike HM, working memory is typically impaired in people with Alzheimer's dementia. However, this form of memory is believed to be linked to the frontal cortex and not the temporal cortex or hippocampus. This explains why HM *was* able to actively rehearse information (because his frontal cortex was not removed during the surgical operation).

Long-term memory: connecting past, present and future

Whereas working memory holds temporary active information 'in mind', **long-term memory** consists of stored information that is acquired in everyday life so that it *persists*, and it can be retrieved long after the experience has occurred. Essentially, information is initially processed in working memory and (it is thought) needs to be passed to the hippocampus so that it can be stored (consolidated) into long-term memory.

Researchers and clinicians have agreed that the long-term memory store can itself be subdivided into **declarative** (or explicit) **memory** and **procedural** (or implicit) **memory**. In addition, declarative memory may be further divided into forms of memory dealing with different types of content: **semantic memory**, relating to facts, events and knowledge about the world; and **episodic memory**, relating to personal associations about particular episodes in life. However, you should note that this division reflects a theoretical and academic approach to the systematic study of memory and these subtypes may, at times, be difficult to separate.

Figure 1.6 presents a simplified version of the currently identified types of long-term memory, to support your understanding of HM's impairments. As you examine it, bear in mind that the area within the dashed lines indicates the types of long-term memory affected following HM's operation. These included his declarative memory and associated subtypes: semantic memory and episodic memory.

On the other hand, HM's procedural memory and his ability to learn (consolidate) motor skills, for example, were not affected by the surgery, which led scientists to conclude that these types of content were *not* processed in the temporal cortex or hippocampus for long-term storage.

In sum, HM's case has revealed three essential facts about memory and the brain. Firstly, that memory is not unitary; there are different types of memory (e.g. working memory and long-term memory). Also that long-term-memory can be subdivided into declarative (or explicit) memory and procedural (or implicit) memory. Finally, that different types of memory are processed by

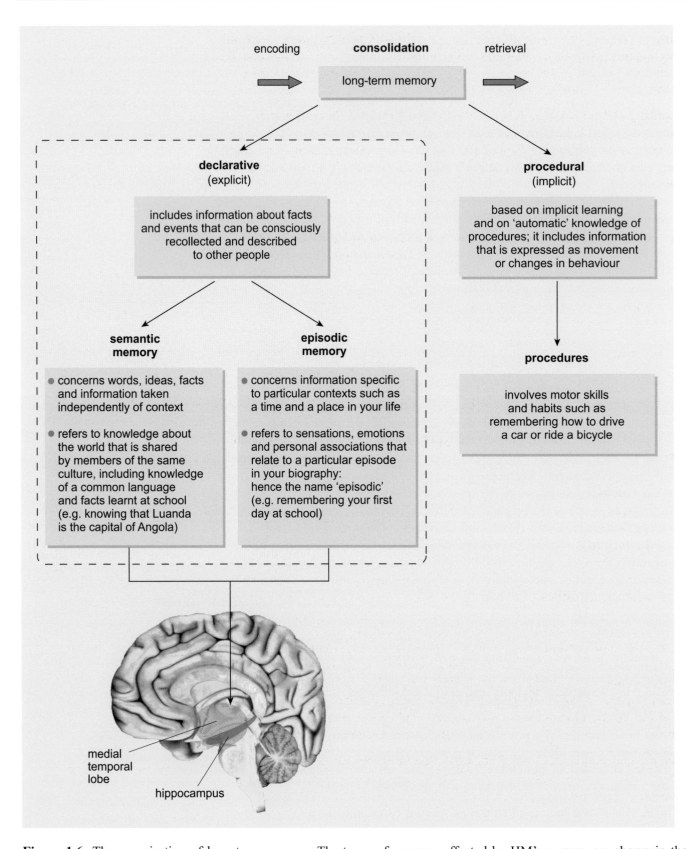

Figure 1.6 The organisation of long-term memory. The types of memory affected by HM's surgery are shown in the area within the dashed lines.

distinct areas of the brain, and that the medial temporal lobes (and specifically the hippocampus) play a fundamental role in the consolidation of declarative memories but not in the consolidation of procedural memories, or in holding information 'in mind' in a working memory.

Similar to HM, most people with Alzheimer's dementia also suffer from a failure to consolidate declarative memories, due to neurodegeneration of the medial temporal lobes, and specifically of the hippocampus. However, in most people with Alzheimer's dementia, procedural memory will be spared, at least initially.

■ What is the difference between anterograde and retrograde amnesia?

☐ Anterograde amnesia refers to the inability to form new memories after a trauma. Retrograde amnesia refers to loss of memory for events directly preceding a trauma.

■ What is the difference between declarative and procedural memory (see Figure 1.6)?

☐ Declarative memory can be consciously recollected and described (or declared) to other people. It includes memory for facts and events. Procedural memory includes non-conscious information that is expressed as movement, motor skills or changes in behaviour.

Alzheimer's dementia affects both subtypes of declarative memory: semantic and episodic.

■ What is the difference between semantic and episodic memory?

☐ Semantic memory refers to general knowledge about the world, including words and concepts and their properties and interrelations. Episodic memory refers to the memory of individual events that are associated with a particular spatial and temporal context. For example, remembering how much you enjoyed your tennis lessons last summer is an episodic memory, whereas knowledge that tennis is a sport is a semantic memory.

We have, in this section, discussed how HM and most people with Alzheimer's dementia have in common the experience of living with anterograde amnesia. Whereas HM lost parts of his temporal cortex and hippocampus due to surgery, many people with AD eventually lose similar areas in their brains due to neuronal degeneration. For this reason, the case of HM can be useful to illustrate how specific and devastating memory impairments can be for people with Alzheimer's dementia.

Having understood more about the organisation of memory and the specific role that the medial temporal cortex and the hippocampus have in consolidating declarative memories, we are now ready to investigate how clinicians may arrive at a diagnosis of Alzheimer's dementia.

1.4 Alzheimer's dementia: giving up memory

Alzheimer's dementia is the most common type of dementia in people aged 65 and older, causing a gradual decline in cognitive abilities, during a typical timespan of 7–10 years. In the early stages of AD, individuals may experience memory impairment, similar to HM, due to neurodegeneration in the temporal lobes.

Traditionally the diagnostic criteria for AD required the presence of multiple cognitive deficits (this essentially means that functions in addition to memory, such as attention or language, should be impaired), evidence of significant impairment in social or occupational functioning, and the confirmation of a suspected dementia syndrome by neuropsychological testing. Until recently, this meant that until a microscopic examination of brain tissue during autopsy had been obtained, the clinical diagnosis remained one of either 'possible' or 'probable' AD. Yet, due to recent technological and scientific advancements, new distinctive and reliable diagnostic tools for AD are becoming available using brain scanning and other techniques (Dubois et al., 2007). You will learn more about these advances in Chapter 2, dedicated to exploring the biology of AD.

1.4.1 Diagnosing Alzheimer's dementia

People with Alzheimer's dementia can benefit considerably from an early diagnosis. The sooner a competent diagnosis is made, the quicker the person will receive appropriate care and treatment. In some cases, early detection may even contribute to delaying the progression of the dementia.

Cultural issues in diagnosing Alzheimer's dementia

Although the idea of providing effective health care as early as possible sounds straightforward, in reality it is not an easy thing to deliver. There are often social and psychological barriers that create particular problems for people with dementia where an early diagnosis may be critical to ensuring a maximal effect of treatments. These barriers may vary across cultures. For example, in some countries (such as India) dementia is not recognised as an organic brain condition that may lead to mental illness. Instead, it is seen as an inevitable consequence of ageing (in Section 1.2.3 it was shown that the evidence does not support this myth). At the same time, if there are no health care systems in place to treat mental health conditions, care is expected to be undertaken by extended family members and to be treated as a 'private' affair, without relying on the state system. This makes it very difficult to identify individuals with the condition.

On the other hand, in countries where health care systems are available, there are other problems that may prevent older people from seeking help at an early stage of AD (as well as other types of dementia). Many individuals may feel embarrassed about their memory problems and may put them down to old age. Lack of acceptance about the severity of the cognitive changes experienced may be another problem that leads individuals to 'bury their heads in the sand', as so often happens when people deal with physical health conditions such as cancer. Others would rather avoid knowing about (or receiving a diagnosis of) a condition for which the outcome is likely to be unfavourable.

In some cases, the fear of disclosing such problems often relates to the stigma associated with dementia. You may recall from Book 1, Chapter 4 that the word 'stigma' refers to a negative social attitude that brands or labels someone. As a result, it is now recognised that there needs to be a focus on educating communities to seek help early in the course of this condition, primarily because researchers have emphasised the need for people with dementia to enter the health care system as early as possible. As you will see in Chapters 3 and 4, the available drug treatments and non-pharmacological therapies work most effectively in the early and middle stages of Alzheimer's dementia. An example of a community health education programme is the '50% campaign' by Alzheimer Scotland (Figure 1.7), so called because the figures startlingly suggest that only 50% of individuals with dementia actually have received a diagnosis of the condition.

Figure 1.7 Photo from the website of Alzheimer Scotland relating to campaigns to increase community awareness of dementia.

Within the UK's multicultural society, such a drive to educate may itself be problematic because a proportion of the population is unable to access and understand information provided by the National Health Service (Oommen et al., 2009). In addition to this, there are problems with the diagnosis of AD in minority ethnic populations in the UK and in populations in non-Western countries worldwide because the assessment instruments have been developed for use in Western populations (Oommen et al., 2009). A focus of research is now to make these assessments culturally appropriate in order to try to solve this problem.

Diagnostic criteria for Alzheimer's dementia

Putting these issues to one side, the diagnostic criteria for AD are essentially similar in the DSM-IV-TR (*Diagnostic and Statistical Manual of Mental Disorders*; APA, 2000) and the ICD-10 (*International Statistical Classification of Diseases and Related Health Problems*; WHO, 1994). According to the

ICD-10, the diagnosis of dementia requires that *each* of the following symptoms is present:

- a decline in memory to an extent that it interferes with everyday activities, or makes independent living either difficult or impossible
- a decline in thinking, planning and organising day-to-day things, again to the above extent
- initially, preserved awareness of the environment, including orientation in space and time
- a decline in emotional control or motivation, or a change in social behaviour, as shown in one or more of the following: emotional lability (or instability); irritability; apathy; coarsening of social behaviour, as in eating, dressing and interacting with others.

Nowadays, a clinician will aim at combining evidence of cognitive impairment (obtained through neuropsychological testing) and hippocampal atrophy (obtained through neuroimaging). Figure 1.8 shows the changes in the brain due to AD revealed by magnetic resonance imaging (MRI), presenting vertical slices (coronal sections) of the brain of a healthy control (on the left) and an AD brain (on the right). Note that the image in (b) shows the generalised widening of the sulci, the considerable enlargement of the lateral ventricles, and, most notable of all, the pronounced bilateral atrophy of the hippocampus (red) and adjacent cortical areas (blue and green).

'Atrophy' refers to loss or diminution in volume.

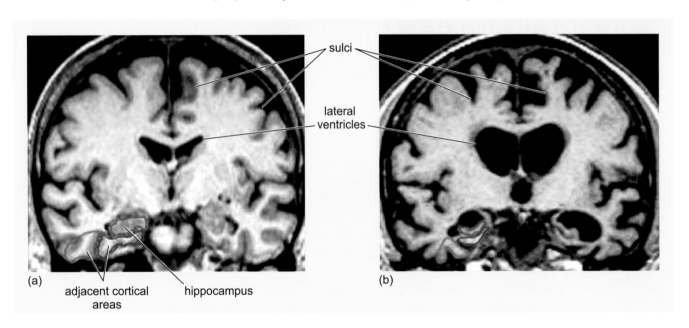

Figure 1.8 Magnetic resonance imaging (MRI) coronal sections of (a) a normal brain and (b) a brain from a person with AD.

Simultaneously, a diagnosis of Alzheimer's dementia requires the clinician to be reasonably sure that any of the cognitive and non-cognitive symptoms (Box 1.1) are measured objectively and verified to be clinically relevant. Clinical relevance is determined by comparing an individual's performance with expected levels of performance for a person's age. The first step of the deficit quantification process (and comparison with a group of similarly aged healthy people, referred to as 'the norm') is called screening. Before screening begins, the clinician will usually explain that a further investigation will only be necessary if evidence of probable Alzheimer's dementia is found. But what exactly is 'evidence' of probable Alzheimer's dementia and how is it measured? We turn to this question in the next section.

Box 1.1 Distinguishing between cognitive and non-cognitive symptoms

Cognitive symptoms (or impairments) refer to problems in the areas of spatial and temporal orientation, attention, memory, thinking, language and basic motor skills.

Non-cognitive symptoms refer to problems detectable as mood disorders, delusions, hallucinations, difficulties in emotional management (e.g. agitation and aggressiveness) and deficits in social skills.

1.4.2 Screening for Alzheimer's dementia: the MMSE

Clinicians have traditionally relied on the Mini Mental State Examination (MMSE; Folstein et al., 1975) to screen people for probable dementia. The MMSE provides a quick snapshot of the person's general cognitive state (Figure 1.9). It includes simple questions and problems in the following areas of functioning:

- orientation, for example the time and place of the test
- registration and recall, for example repeating and remembering lists of words
- attention, for example writing a series of numbers
- language use and comprehension
- basic motor skills.

For example, is the person oriented in time and space? Can they memorise bits of information and manipulate objects in their minds? Can they follow instructions? These are some of the questions being explored with this test.

The MMSE is regarded as an effective and easy-to-administer tool that can also be used to document cognitive changes over time. People with dementia tire easily, so quicker assessments are preferred in practice. The MMSE takes about 10 minutes to administer so it is ideal.

The MMSE has a maximum score of 30 points, and scores below 25 suggest probable cases of mild dementia that should be further investigated, also known by clinicians as the 'cut-off' point. However, it is not as straightforward as this. Clinicians need to correct (or adjust) a score obtained on the MMSE for a person's educational attainment and age. Obtained scores (known as **raw scores**) express the number of correct answers a person achieves without taking into consideration other factors that are known to

Mini Mental State Examination

1. **Orientation:**
   * What is the (year) (season) (month) (date) (day) ?
   * Where are we? (country) (county) (town) (hospital) (floor)

2. **Registration:**
   * Identify and name 3 objects
     (e.g. pen, book, chair)
   * Repeat names of 3 objects until learnt

3. **Attention and Calculation:**
   * Write a series of the number 7
   * Spell 'world' backwards
     (score is equal to number of correct letters before
     first mistake; i.e. 'dlorw' = 2 correct)

4. **Recall:**
   * Recall the objects named in Section 2.

5. **Language:**
   * Repeat: 'no ifs, ands or buts'
   * Follow a 3-stage command, e.g.
     'Take the paper in your right hand, fold it in half, and put it
     on the floor.'
   * Read and obey a command, e.g.
     Close your eyes
     Write a sentence spontaneously
     Copy design below

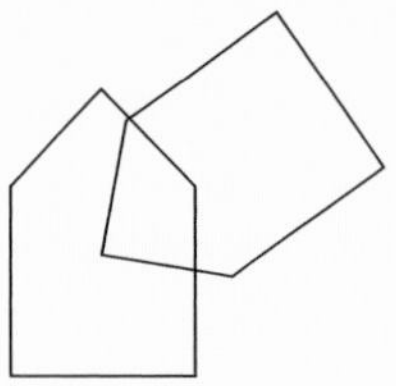

Total: 30 points

Figure 1.9 Examples of tasks in the Mini Mental State Examination (MMSE). Each section scores a different number of points, with a total score of 30.

affect performance on this test (such as age or educational background). Recent evidence suggests that, in the case of very well-educated individuals, the cut-off point for dementia should be raised to 27 for higher sensitivity (O'Bryant et al., 2008). What this means is that, by the time a well-educated individual scores 25 on the MMSE, the dementia is more advanced than it would be in an individual with an average educational background.

In general, low to very low scores (generally, below 17 points) correlate very closely with the probability of dementia, although you should note that other mental or physical conditions can also lead to low scores on the MMSE. For example, people with difficulties in hearing or reading, or those with motor deficits that may affect their writing and drawing skills can obtain low scores on this test.

Although the MMSE is more effective for the assessment of cognitive symptoms of AD, it may be used to screen for other types of dementia such as frontotemporal and vascular dementia. However, its use for the assessment of frontotemporal dementia is less effective, as the onset of this dementia is marked by non-cognitive rather than cognitive changes.

1.4.3 Functional diagnosis: the CDR and the FAST

Functional diagnosis is the second step of the assessment process. It is applied to all types of dementia and focuses on establishing differences in the person's cognition, personality, behavioural manifestations or daily living activities, between their premorbid (before the symptoms) and current level of functioning. Essentially, the clinician is looking for three main markers of dementia:

- Is the difference significant – how much has the person changed?
- The time course of the change – how fast has the change occurred?
- The pattern of change across the various cognitive processes (such as attention, memory, language), personality characteristics and general behaviour – in what way have changes occurred?

To help you put this information into context, we now return to the case of Filip (Vignette 1.4), whose changes are described by Anna, his wife.

Vignette 1.4 Diagnosing Alzheimer's dementia: Filip's case

Then our youngest daughter got engaged. But to my surprise, Filip wasn't as interested as he normally would be. Usually he'd be very fussy about making the arrangements. Instead, he became quite passive. Anyway, the wedding happened, and we retired soon after. I then noticed that he started becoming unsure of himself and would say, 'Will you put on the washing' or 'Will you make lunch'. At the golf course I noticed that he was forgetting his score and wondering which club to use. Soon after, I realised that Filip was neglecting his beloved garden: he often forgot to water his plants, he would plant seeds at the wrong times, and let the weeds run wild. A few weeks later, he could not make sense of his bank statement and got into a rage over the phone with his account manager.

Finally, our GP arranged for him to see a consultant for screening and further tests. I was told that Filip had probable Alzheimer's. He was barely 60. After the diagnosis we stayed at home, and I think I over-protected him. I never let him leave the house on his own. That was fine for about four years and we led a very nice life. By then I had to tag items around the house to help Filip find his way (Figure 1.10). Then about five years later, a friend, who's a psycho-geriatrician, suggested he should be admitted to the day hospital so that I could have a break.

A psychogeriatrician is a psychiatrist who specialises in the treatment and care of older people.

Figure 1.10 Within four years of being diagnosed, Filip had forgotten how to get around his home, so the tags helped him remember where things were.

That worked well for a couple of years, but then Filip started walking more slowly, which we knew was common with Alzheimer's. There were also times when he didn't feel well. A few months ago he fell in the shower whilst I ran out to get fresh towels, so now I always help him when he is in the bathroom, either during bathing or for the rest. I must also help him to get dressed to make sure he always wears fresh clothes.

■ When screened using the MMSE, Filip scored 22. How can you interpret this result?

☐ A score of 22 is below the cut-off point (25). This suggests that Filip may have dementia.

Filip's case was investigated by the consultant to evaluate which other areas of his functioning (thinking and planning, social skills, emotions, daily living skills) were impaired. Also, considering that Filip is well-educated (you may recall that he is a retired GP), his score gains particular relevance when compared with the suggested cut-off for well-educated individuals (27).

There are several ways to obtain information on how much (and how fast) a person has changed since the manifestation of Alzheimer's dementia signs and symptoms. As described in Book 1, Section 4.3, the person with dementia and a close informant are interviewed and a clinical history is taken. Ideally, urine and blood samples are collected in order to exclude several systemic diseases. An electroencephalogram is taken and neuroimaging of the brain is performed using magnetic resonance imaging (MRI) or other available methods. (We will return to these methods in Chapter 2.)

■ What would the clinician's focus be while undertaking a functional diagnosis?

☐ How much the person has changed since the first signs and symptoms manifested, how fast and in what ways specifically.

In practice, it is nearly impossible to pinpoint the moment of the onset of Alzheimer's dementia. However, and as a rule of thumb, if there is no relevant knowledge about the individual, it may be assumed that his or her premorbid functioning was normal in comparison with other similarly aged persons, with comparable levels of education and professional interests.

Several scales may be used during functional diagnosis and we will concentrate on two of them: the CDR and FAST.

The CDR

The Clinical Dementia Rating Scale (CDR; Morris, 1993) is a numeric scale, widely used to quantify the severity of the symptoms of dementia in six areas of functioning: memory, orientation, judgement and problem solving, community affairs, home and hobbies, and personal care. The information is gathered during an interview with the person with dementia and their carer. The CDR scores include 0 (no dementia), 0.5 (questionable), 1 (mild), 2 (moderate) and 3 (severe). As an example, the CDR's memory subscale would be scored in the following way:

- none (0): no memory loss or slight inconsistent forgetfulness
- questionable (0.5): consistent slight forgetfulness; partial recollection of events; 'benign forgetfulness'
- mild (1): moderate memory loss, more marked for recent events; deficit interferes with everyday activity
- moderate (2): severe memory loss, only highly learned material retained; new material rapidly lost
- severe (3): severe memory loss, only fragments remain.

On the other hand, the personal care subscale would be scored thus:

- none (0): fully capable of self-care
- questionable (0.5): consistent partial failure of self-care
- mild (1): needs prompting
- moderate (2): requires assistance with dressing, hygiene and organisation of personal belongings
- severe (3): requires much help with personal care; frequent incontinence.

Although the CDR has a reputation for being sensitive to very mild impairments, it relies on a *subjective* assessment of the person's situation, which may be limiting, considering that people's interpretations of events vary considerably from individual to individual. It also takes a long time to administer compared with the MMSE. We now turn to the FAST.

There are further ratings on the CDR subscales for assessing the end stages of dementia.

The FAST

The Functional Assessment Staging Test (FAST) is a 16-item scale designed to mirror the characteristic progression of functional loss in Alzheimer's dementia. It discriminates seven major levels of functioning, from normal ageing to severe AD, and includes 11 substages that help differentiate subtle differences that may signal progression from moderately severe to severe dementia (see Figure 1.11). Stages 2 and 3 define an intermediate stage between normal ageing and dementia known as mild cognitive impairment, or MCI. As you will see in Section 1.4.6, some people with MCI remain stable or return to normal over time, but some may progress to dementia.

Stage	Diagnosis	Main characteristics	Average MMSE scores
Stage 1	Normal ageing	No deficits, either subjectively or objectively	29–30
Stage 2	Possible mild cognitive impairment	Complaints of forgetting location of objects. Subjective functional deficits	28–29
Stage 3	Mild cognitive impairment	Decreased job functioning evident to co-workers. Difficulty in travelling to new locations. Decreased organisational capacity.	24–28
Stage 4	Mild dementia	Decreased ability to perform complex tasks, e.g. planning dinner for guests, handling personal finances (such as forgetting to pay bills), difficulty in shopping for groceries, etc.	19–20
Stage 5	Moderate dementia	Needs help selecting appropriate clothing	15
Stage 6	Moderately severe dementia	(a) Needs help putting on clothes (b) Needs help bathing (c) Needs help with using the toilet (d) Urinary incontinence (more frequently over the past weeks) (e) Fecal incontinence (more frequently over the past weeks)	9 8 5 3 1
Stage 7	Severe dementia	(a) Speaks 5–6 words during a day (b) Speaks only one word clearly (c) Can no longer walk (d) Can no longer sit up (e) Can no longer smile (f) Can no longer hold head up	0 0 0 0 0 0

Figure 1.11 The functional assessment staging test (FAST). Average MMSE scores are shown in the final column for comparison.

Rather than evaluating the individual's cognitive and non-cognitive symptoms (Box 1.1), the FAST focuses on what they are able to do, often relying on carer reports gathered during an interview. A clinician who has been treating a person with AD for five years, and has used the FAST in each visit (longitudinally, Book 1, Box 4.5), will be able to evaluate the effectiveness of a given treatment by determining how many months the person has spent in a particular stage. So, for example, the average expected untreated duration of stage 4 (which includes difficulty in performing complex tasks such as managing finances) is 24 months. If the FAST results show that the person has remained at stage 4 for 47 months, this would indicate that the treatment has delayed the progression of AD by 23 months.

Note that although the FAST is useful in charting change and evaluating treatment effectiveness, it remains very difficult to predict how Alzheimer's dementia (as any other type of dementia) will progress, as the course of the condition will vary from individual to individual (see Activity 1.2).

The FAST is also a useful tool to determine if changes in a person's condition are due to AD or another condition. We will return to this issue in the next section, dedicated to differential diagnosis.

■ Why is it important that the FAST is able to demonstrate validity?

☐ Validity (Book 1, Section 4.2.4) ensures that the FAST measures what it is intended to measure and therefore that the results are useful to discriminate changes in the person's levels of functional impairment.

Activity 1.2 Living with AD

(LO 1.3) Allow 20 minutes

This activity on the multimedia map illustrates how dementia may affect the three spheres of a person's life – the 'bio', 'psycho' and 'social'. It also exemplifies how predictions about the course of this condition and how the person will be affected are notoriously difficult to make.

1.4.4 Differential diagnosis

You may now recall the concept of differential diagnosis to which you were introduced in Book 1, Section 4.3.4, as the process of weighing up the probability of one disorder versus that of other disorders that may account for a person's illness.

Vignette 1.5 illustrates a typical situation in which members of a mental health team (Book 1, Section 4.1.2) will be required to make a differential diagnosis between Alzheimer's dementia and depression. Often older people are depressed, unmotivated, disorganised and may come across as showing signs and symptoms of dementia, when in fact they may have a mood disorder. The issue is further complicated because those who find that they have memory problems may well become depressed by the changes that they are experiencing.

The World Health Organization (WHO) guidelines recommend that, when diagnosing dementia, clinicians should rule out the following alternative diagnoses:

• depressive disorders, which may exhibit many of the features of an early dementia, especially memory impairment, slowed thinking, apathy and lack of spontaneity

- delirium, which typically is acute in onset with clouding of consciousness, fluctuating in degree

- mild or moderate mental retardation

- premorbid states (developed before the current condition) of subnormal cognitive functioning attributable to a severely impoverished social environment and limited education

- iatrogenic (medically caused) mental disorders.

The MMSE is particularly useful when clinicians are asked to make a differential diagnosis between AD and depression because it quickly identifies whether there are any cognitive symptoms (Box 1.1) associated with AD. For example, when answering the 'orientation' questions (Figure 1.9), a person with depression is likely to be oriented, whereas a person with AD will have probably lost track of the date and the type of premises (a clinic, for example) and the town where they are being examined. Also, whereas a person with depression will still be able to follow specific instructions relating to language (such as 'take the paper in your *right* hand, fold it in *half*, and put it on the *floor*'), a person with Alzheimer's dementia will probably get confused.

So, is Bill (Vignette 1.5) at the onset of Alzheimer's dementia or is he depressed? This distinction is crucial because whereas dementia is likely to compromise his autonomy and put him at immediate risk (he lives alone), depression can be managed towards a more positive outcome. Yet, they may be easily confused at times.

Figure 1.12 Is Bill showing signs of dementia or is he depressed?

Vignette 1.5 Differentiating dementia and depression: Bill's case

Bill is 77 and a retired librarian (Figure 1.12). Lately he has become forgetful and has not paid some of his gas and electricity bills. He also forgets to take his medicines, so had to call an ambulance about two months ago when he felt very poorly due to high blood pressure. Nurses from the local mental health team now visit him regularly. During the first few visits Bill stayed mute and avoided eye contact most of the time. Recently, however, he opened up and reported that it all changed for him when he lost his wife about six months ago. Then Shirley, his only daughter, had to move up north with the children. Now, he just sits in front of the television most afternoons and has not attended his book club meetings. He only leaves the house to get groceries and the paper from the local shops. According to the nurse's report, he is a vegetarian and still cooks two meals a day. The house is in relatively good order. Bill was screened for dementia and scored 28 in the MMSE.

■ Does Bill have dementia? Explain your answer.

☐ No. Bill is probably depressed. His forgetfulness seems to be related to feelings of sadness and isolation, rather than the range of symptoms associated with dementia. It can also be explained by a series of events in his life. Although his thinking is slowed and he shows apathy, Bill is still able to communicate, retains his independence and is able to plan and organise his day-to-day activities, including shopping, reading the paper and cooking his favourite vegetarian meals. He is also keeping his flat in reasonably good order. Finally, his MMSE score is above the cut-off point.

1.4.5 Understanding normal age-related memory decline

With age, along with the expected physical decline, there may be a relative loss of cognitive ability. Consequently, a relevant concern for most people of any mature age is to decide whether they should worry about their self-perceived cognitive decline. 'Could this mean the onset of dementia? Should I be seeing a specialist?' So, a critical question is: how is it possible to differentiate normal age-related cognitive loss from the early onset of dementia? In this section, we'll discuss normal age-related memory loss from a clinical perspective and we will clarify which types of memory may be affected by normal ageing. First, however, you will read about Norma who is 71 and worried about her memory (Vignette 1.6).

> ### Vignette 1.6 Ageing and memory loss: Norma's experience
>
> My name is Norma. I'm 71 years old and semi-retired. Six years ago I retired from a long career in a big accountancy firm in Bristol but I still run my own small business and look after the accounts of a handful of clients because it keeps me busy. I like to be kept busy! But I'm not as sharp as I used to be and I'm worried. I used to know the times tables by heart. Well, I was trained way before they invented electronic calculators so doing the odd multiplication in my head was never a problem for me. Well, it is now. Do you know I sometimes forget meetings with my clients, or deadlines to pay bills? I have booked an appointment with my GP because I honestly don't know what I would do without my Blackberry. That's where I write it all down so that I can keep track of things.

From the clinical perspective, people with normal age-related cognitive loss and people with dementia will differ in terms of the *range* of cognitive domains (or mental processes) being affected and how *severely* each of the domains is affected. These are important concepts to remember: range and severity, as they help the clinician make judgements about whether a person may have dementia or not.

Clinical differences between dementia and normal age-related memory loss

Let us concentrate on the issue of range first. Whilst people with normal age-related decline will tend to experience some difficulties in *a specific* cognitive domain – typically memory – a person with dementia will show impairments in *several* cognitive domains *simultaneously*; this could include: attention, memory, thinking and planning, as well as a range of social and emotional skills (see Section 1.4.1 on the diagnostic criteria for Alzheimer's dementia). An example of the first case would be Norma (Vignette 1.6) and an example of the second could be Filip (Vignette 1.4).

Secondly, whereas a person with normal age-related memory decline will feel a slight deficiency, which is usually classified as subclinical, people with Alzheimer's dementia have *severe* and *disabling* impairments that will soon compromise their autonomy and may put them (or others) at risk. Again, Filip, for example, has severe memory impairment as well as difficulties functioning in everyday life. His planning is poor. You may recall that he planted seeds at the wrong time and couldn't choose the appropriate golf club during his golfing rounds. He has lost his autonomy and requires full-time care. But how does that compare with Norma?

The term 'subclinical' refers to the absence of a clear pattern of signs and symptoms.

Well, although Norma has concerns about her memory problems, she still carries out her everyday activities and does not have problems in other areas of her cognition. Notice that she has learnt how to operate a fairly modern gadget as a strategy to compensate for her memory loss. So, the main difference is that she is in control of her life and illustrates what specialists refer to as normal age-related memory decline.

The effect of age on memory subtypes

In Section 1.3 you learnt that memory is not unitary and specific aspects are disrupted in Alzheimer's dementia. But, in a healthy population, what types of memories are expected to decline and from what age is the decline thought to begin?

To find out answers to these questions, the Betula study, based at the University of Stockholm, researched memory performance longitudinally in 3600 healthy Swedish participants, aged 35–80. The evidence from one of their studies suggests that the four memory systems tested – working memory, declarative (semantic and episodic) and procedural memory – age at different rates (Nilsson, 2003).

So, which type of memory seems to decline faster? According to the evidence, episodic memory shows a sharper decrease after the age of 60 than other types of memory (see Figure 1.13). By contrast, procedural memory (well-learnt motor skills) seems to stay stable and constant across the lifespan (not shown in Figure 1.13).

Note that the results in Figure 1.13 are presented in the form of standard scores (otherwise know as *z*-scores). This method of presenting results is discussed in Box 1.2.

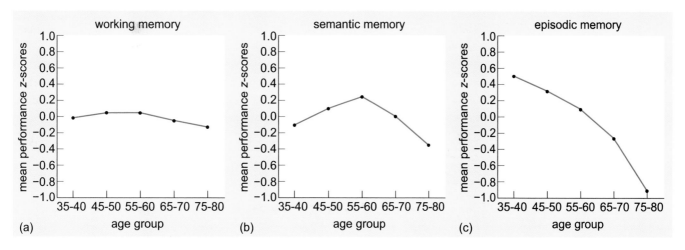

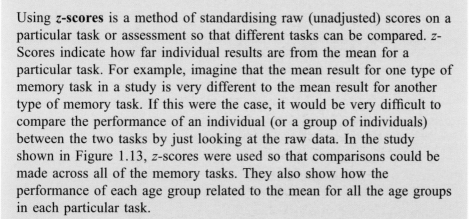

Figure 1.13 Mean performance as a function of age in tasks assessing (a) working memory, (b) semantic memory, and (c) episodic memory.

Box 1.2 Research Methods: Understanding z-scores

Using **z-scores** is a method of standardising raw (unadjusted) scores on a particular task or assessment so that different tasks can be compared. z-Scores indicate how far individual results are from the mean for a particular task. For example, imagine that the mean result for one type of memory task in a study is very different to the mean result for another type of memory task. If this were the case, it would be very difficult to compare the performance of an individual (or a group of individuals) between the two tasks by just looking at the raw data. In the study shown in Figure 1.13, z-scores were used so that comparisons could be made across all of the memory tasks. They also show how the performance of each age group related to the mean for all the age groups in each particular task.

So, how do z-scores work? In psychology it is reasonable to assume that the spread of all results on a task or assessment will fall into a **normal distribution curve**, which means that the results are equally distributed either side of the mean result (Figure 1.14). The exact centre of the peak of the curve will be the mean value, as indicated on the graph. A z-score simply converts the obtained mean value of a set of results to a value of 0 (zero).

Now, recall that the standard deviation (SD) is a measure of the spread of a set of results around the mean value (Book 2, Box 1.3). A score that is precisely the value of the standard deviation above the mean will be given a z-score value of +1, and a score that is twice the value of the standard deviation above the mean will be given a z-score value of +2, and so on. Scores below the mean will be given negative z-scores (this can be seen in Figure 1.14). In the study shown in Figure 1.13, scores were standardised for each of the memory tasks using the mean for all age groups together in each task.

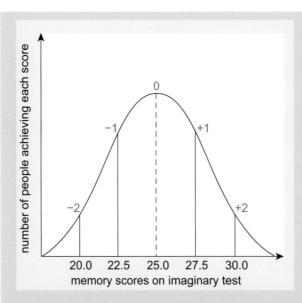

Figure 1.14 A normal distribution curve of memory scores from the general population. The *z*-scores are shown in red.

z-Scores are particularly useful in clinical psychology because they can be used to judge 'abnormal performance'. Let's use the example of a set of memory task results taken from a sample of the general population. This sample would be referred to as the reference population (or 'the norm', Section 1.4.1). The mean value from this sample (let's imagine it was 25, as shown in Figure 1.14) would be given a *z*-score of 0. Now imagine that the SD of the memory scores from this reference population was 2.5. Abnormal performance on any assessment or task is judged as a *z*-score of +2 (or higher) or −2 (or lower).

- Considering the criteria above, imagine that an individual obtains a score of 20 on the same memory task. Would this score be judged as abnormal based on the reference population scores?

- Yes it would be abnormal. A score of 20 is 2 SDs below the reference population mean and would be given a *z*-score of −2.

So, to summarise, a *z*-score gives an indication of the distance of the raw score from the mean score of a task and can be used to compare results across different tasks or to judge abnormal performance in a particular task.

Earlier research on cognitive ageing has been mainly based on cross-sectional analyses (Book 1, Box 4.5) of data, which had suggested a progressive steady decline in performance from the age of about 20 years! However, longitudinal data from the Betula project show a completely different pattern. Note that cross-sectional data *estimate* how individual memory abilities may change by comparing groups of different ages, whereas longitudinal studies actually assess the same participants over several years.

■ What does Figure 1.13a show?

☐ The figure suggests a relatively stable performance level in working memory across all age groups, indicating no age deficit. In other words, the data show that the normal ageing process does not affect working memory.

■ What does Figure 1.13b show?

☐ The figure shows that there is an increase in performance in semantic memory from 35–40 years to 55–60 years, after which there is a noticeable decrease.

In summary, whereas normal age-related memory loss can be quantified as subclinical, memory impairments typical of dementia are severe. Also, longitudinal evidence from the Betula study suggests that normal ageing may account for some decline in episodic and semantic memory, but may not necessarily affect the person's working or procedural memory.

There is, however, more to this story. Researchers and clinicians began to wonder whether there was an intermediate stage between normal ageing and dementia which could be defined clinically as:

• cognitive decline *greater* than that expected for an individual's age and educational level, but

• *not* clinically significant enough to warrant a diagnosis of dementia.

This intermediate syndrome has been termed **mild cognitive impairment (MCI)**, and the hope is that it will help clinicians predict the onset of AD long before a diagnosis would usually be made, effectively enabling earlier and more effective interventions. This issue is discussed in the next section.

1.4.6 Mild cognitive impairment

This section concentrates on a particular form of MCI called 'amnestic MCI'. Individuals given this diagnosis typically present with memory impairments greater than normal age-related memory loss but there is no impairment of daily living. Alternatively, other individuals falling into the category of 'non-amnestic MCI' usually have *one or more* impairments in domains other than memory and again no impairment of daily living (Golomb et al., 2004; European Alzheimer's Disease Consortium, 2010). This difference is critical because amnestic MCI individuals are hypothesised to develop Alzheimer's dementia, whereas non-amnestic MCI individuals are hypothesised to develop frontotemporal or vascular dementia.

The term 'amnestic' refers to the presence of memory-related symptoms.

So, is there strong evidence that amnestic MCI leads to Alzheimer's dementia? In a study by Petersen et al. (1999), it was shown that nearly 50% of the 76 amnestic MCI individuals studied (average age 80) developed Alzheimer's dementia within a period of 48 months (Figure 1.15). These data can be used to calculate the **annual conversion rate** (ACR), defined as the percentage of individuals who develop a disorder within a 12-month period. The ACR for AD in healthy controls with similar ages varied between 1 and 2%. The ACR was therefore much higher for individuals in the MCI group compared with healthy controls. Note that a link between MCI and AD should

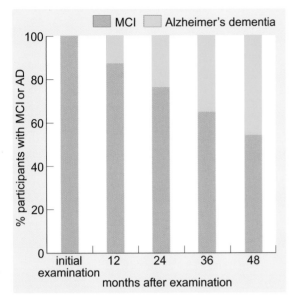

Figure 1.15 Annual rates of conversion from amnestic MCI to Alzheimer's dementia over 48 months (Petersen et al., 1999).

be demonstrated through high ACRs, which indicate how many MCI individuals actually progress to dementia within a year.

■ What does Figure 1.15 show?

□ It demonstrates the outcome for the participants with amnestic MCI within a period of four years. The data show that the ACR of these individuals was 12% so that by the end of the fourth year nearly half (4 × 12% = 48%) had developed Alzheimer's dementia.

Taken at face value, these high ACRs would suggest that amnestic MCI is a clinically recognisable intermediate stage between normal ageing and AD. This could be good news for enhancing early diagnosis of AD.

However, the evidence about the power of MCI as a predictor of Alzheimer's dementia is far from conclusive. Mitchell and Shiri-Feshki (2009) performed a meta-analysis of 41 longitudinal studies that had collected data for longer than three years, and they reported a much lower ACR of only 5–10% for amnestic MCI individuals. More importantly, other studies have shown that up to 44% of individuals who had received a diagnosis of MCI (both amnestic and non-amnestic) at their first visit to a clinic were estimated to have returned to normal a year later (Ritchie, 2004; Ganguli et al., 2004). These findings suggest that many cases of MCI may be reversible, or possibly misdiagnosed, calling into question the usefulness of MCI as a predictor of dementia.

Additionally, recent evidence has brought to light that many (if not all) amnestic MCI individuals tend to hide other subtle cognitive deficits (besides memory difficulties), which compromises the initial definition of memory problems as the main precursor of Alzheimer's dementia (Salmon and Hodges, 2005).

Thus the current concept of amnestic MCI does not seem to capture the full spectrum of the condition. Because not all individuals with amnestic MCI will progress to overt AD, the identification and refinement of cognitive, genetic and biological markers that might allow the definition and detection of an early stage of Alzheimer's dementia and the prediction of its course remains a clinical research priority.

1.4.7 Caring for someone with Alzheimer's dementia

You may remember that when you met Martha, a distinguished professor of genetics, at the beginning of the chapter (Vignette 1.1) she had already been transformed by the devastating effects of neurodegeneration. On average, people with Alzheimer's dementia may typically live for 7–10 years after they are diagnosed, although some may live as long as 20 years after diagnosis. There seems to be, however, an important milestone in the progression of AD: once non-memory functions also begin to decline, mental deterioration proceeds more rapidly. Within that timespan, nearly all brain functions, including memory, movement, language, judgement, behaviour and abstract thinking, will be eventually affected, as described by Anna (Vignette 1.7).

Filip is now in the 15th year since his diagnosis, and probably the 17th or 18th year of his illness.

Vignette 1.7 Caring for someone with late-stage Alzheimer's dementia: Anna's advice

There isn't much left of the man I used to know. He's extremely unwell and lies in the fetal position, but he has been beautifully looked after. He receives proper nutrition, proper hydration, beautiful skin care, and his bladder problems are dealt with expertly. He still seems to enjoy his food, and he's never had a bed sore. I recognise that some people would say, 'What's the point?', but as far as I'm concerned, his quality of life is good. We celebrated our Golden wedding anniversary in June.

From a carer's perspective, you go through stages. The first stage starts before the diagnosis. That's very awkward. It's a difficult time for the person with the illness, and for the loved ones looking after them, as well as for the professionals. It's not an easy diagnosis, and it takes great skill and expertise. But if you're worried about the situation, don't put off finding out what's happening. Get it investigated.

Then there's the stage after diagnosis. It's important to remember that this diagnosis isn't disastrous. Initially I thought it was, but it wasn't. And people with Alzheimer's don't become a different person overnight. It happens gradually, and people should be encouraged to live as normal and fruitful a life as possible, whatever a normal life means! Don't just sit there and do nothing.

I'm a volunteer and help to run carer support groups. I've also helped to set up the Alzheimer's Café for Carers. Carers are often on their own, and this café gives them a chance to meet one another and release their emotions. They can also bring their loved ones along. We also have days out. Keeping people out of isolation is so important because carers tend to become isolated. Judging from my own experience, you tend to keep to yourself. I'd say that one of the best things carers can do is join carer support groups. Meet other carers, share experiences and support one another. You can learn an awful lot.

We will examine in detail the treatment and care of people with Alzheimer's dementia in the remainder of this book. The next two sections of this chapter explore the signs and symptoms, as well as causes and prognosis, of the other forms of dementia discussed at the start of the book: frontotemporal dementia and vascular dementia.

1.5 Frontotemporal dementia: giving up the emotions

Frontotemporal dementia involves neurodegeneration in the frontal cortex initially (Figure 1.16), which later may extend to the temporal cortex. (By contrast, the neurodegeneration in Alzheimer's dementia may extend from the temporal cortex to the frontal cortex in the later stages.) The frontal lobes can be thought of as our 'management' (i.e. executive) centre, as well as our emotional monitoring centre and home to our personality. They are involved in the ability to focus attention, speak, generate strategies, make good judgements and control our impulses. If it is said that Alzheimer's dementia takes away a person's ability to memorise, frontotemporal dementia takes away a person's ability to manage their emotions.

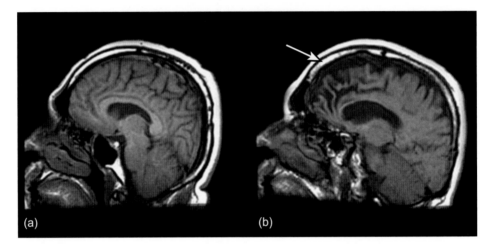

Figure 1.16 Scan of (a) a typical brain and (b) a brain from a person with frontotemporal dementia showing neurodegeneration and atrophy in the frontal lobes (indicated by the arrow).

This could explain Morag's self-abandonment and isolation. You may recall (Vignette 1.2) that she had been found lying in her own urine surrounded by litter and unwilling to ask for help. We now turn to Vignette 1.8 and the case of Sally who illustrates some further signs and symptoms of frontotemporal dementia, as told by her brother Brian.

Vignette 1.8 Frontotemporal dementia: Sally's case

After we arrived at the hospital I asked them to run an MRI because Sally had had a brain tumour some years ago. After the MRI was examined I was told that she had a head trauma from a car accident. I knew she hadn't and kept pressing for more tests. They ran a CT scan and then another consultant looked again at her MRI and saw the disease. This had nothing to do with the brain tumour.

She began forgetting to go to appointments and had problems concentrating; she started getting angry at other drivers when driving, forgetting to pay bills and having crying episodes at work. Three months ago she had an incident where she got mad and threw a box at someone. Colleagues also began complaining about her either rude or inappropriate sexual comments, both quite uncharacteristic of the Sally everyone had known and worked with. Very often she would come into the office and change into clothes she had just bought; except she did it in front of everyone. Interestingly, it took some time for anyone to pay attention to what was happening.

After that we had to put her on disability and take away her driving privileges. This has been hard for her to understand because she thinks she is fine. The hardest part for me was telling the doctors (in front of her) what was going on.

This is only the beginning, I know, and I must find the courage to talk to her about plans for her future. I am her only brother. Our parents are 82 and 83 and they are in better health than my sister who is 56. It has been eight months, and I finally have her house clean. The dementia itself is enough to deal with. Now, I also have to take care of her financial and medical decisions. I make sure that I still make the time to enjoy my three grandchildren and go away periodically with my wife and do nothing. Absolutely nothing. Right now she is at the point where she is child-like and does not want to bathe, brush her teeth or go to bed.

Progressively, individuals with frontotemporal dementia become isolated in their own world, due to a lack of emotional rapport with those around them. Frontal lobe damage leads to a dramatic change in social behaviour, where the person may become disinhibited, showing lack of judgement, and have difficulties in controlling their behaviour as illustrated by Sally's story. The course of brain damage is different from that observed in AD, which explains the different signs and symptoms.

Overall, frontotemporal dementia affects about 1 in 5000 of the general population, and usually occurs well before the age of 65, affecting both genders equally. Morag was only 57 and Sally only 56 when diagnosed. After 65 years of age the disorder occurs only rarely. A family history of a similar condition is common, with as many as half of people affected reporting an affected brother or sister, cousin, parent or grandparent. The duration of the condition is often about 10–15 years, which is comparatively longer than the typical duration of Alzheimer's dementia or vascular dementia.

Frontotemporal dementia may be very difficult to diagnose, given its early onset, especially as the timing of onset can coincide with major changes in a person's life (such as the start of the menopause in women). The fact that it typically manifests mainly through non-cognitive symptoms (Box 1.1), which are difficult to screen for with the MMSE, also makes it difficult to detect. Major functional changes in people with this type of dementia can be picked up by the CDR and FAST, but only relatively late in the course of the dementia.

Activity 1.3 Living with frontotemporal dementia
(LO 1.3) Allow 30 minutes

Go to the multimedia map and listen to the interviews with Victoria who has cared for Nick, her husband, who was diagnosed with semantic dementia at the age of 52 (semantic dementia is a variant of frontotemporal dementia).

1.5.1 Signs and symptoms of frontotemporal dementia

As illustrated by Morag (Vignette 1.3a), Sally (Vignette 1.8) and Nick (Activity 1.3), people with frontotemporal dementia typically show dramatic personality changes and lack of control over their own behaviour. Initially, they may become uninhibited and restless. More often than not, they have to give up work through failure to concentrate or as a result of antisocial attitudes and actions towards their colleagues. In later stages of the dementia, the person becomes less interested in their environment and may limit their range of behaviours, often to a repetitive series of rituals typically involving hoarding, gluttony and food fads.

Individuals frequently lose insight into their illness and progressively become unable to show care and sympathy towards friends and family. As the effects of the condition progress to the temporal lobes, there may be language impairment as the person 'loses' the meaning of words, fails to recognise and name objects or people, or becomes unable to generate speech with proper construction of phrases and sentences.

■ What, in Sally's behaviour, suggests that she is at an early stage of frontotemporal dementia?

□ She has difficulties concentrating, and in planning any sort of activity. She has missed appointments and has difficulties controlling her behaviour, all of which imply impaired frontal lobe processing.

■ Why is it difficult to diagnose frontotemporal dementia?

□ The onset of frontotemporal dementia usually happens during the person's late forties or early fifties and tends to be confounded with major emotional changes that may occur at this time (e.g. the menopause or redundancy). Also, its mainly non-cognitive symptoms are difficult to detect using conventional screening tools for dementia, such as the MMSE.

1.5.2 Causes of frontotemporal dementia

In about half of cases of frontotemporal dementia, the condition is inherited due to a chromosomal mutation in the gene that makes **tau** protein, a protein involved in normal neuronal functioning. (You will learn more about this protein in Chapter 2 of this book because an abnormal formation of tau is one of the pathological hallmarks of Alzheimer's dementia.) So far, at least 30 different mutations in the *tau* gene linked to frontotemporal dementia have been identified.

It is also likely that several other genetic changes may be responsible for causing the condition, and current research is concentrating on identifying changes in at least two other genes on different chromosomes. However, in the remaining individuals who do not show such genetic changes, the cause of the illness is still unknown. Within this group, many individuals have no family history of frontotemporal dementia, and there is uncertainty as to whether any genetic susceptibility to the dementia exists, or whether there are non-genetic or environmental causes at play.

1.5.3   Treatment, course and prognosis of frontotemporal dementia

No treatment has been shown to slow the progression of frontotemporal dementia, which means that the outcome is poor. In some cases, aggressive, agitated or dangerous behaviours may be controlled through behaviour management therapy (Section 4.3) or through medication. Antidepressants have been shown to improve some symptoms. The dementia progresses steadily and often rapidly. It may take somewhere between two years and more than 10 years to arrive at the stage of requiring round-the-clock care and monitoring, either at home or in an institutionalised care setting.

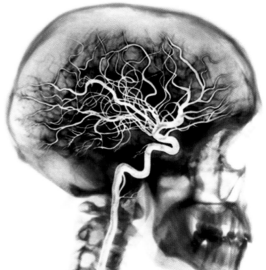

Figure 1.17 The network of blood vessels supplying oxygen and nutrients to the brain.

1.6   Vascular dementia: giving up the self

Vascular dementia is the second most common form of dementia after Alzheimer's dementia, accounting for up to one-quarter of all dementias. An additional 20% of all people with dementia may have both Alzheimer's and vascular dementia. Vascular dementia is not a single condition, but rather a group of syndromes relating to different vascular mechanisms thought to impair blood supply to the brain (Figure 1.17). This explains why Joy may have very different symptoms from other people with vascular dementia. You may recall (Vignette 1.3b) that she started wandering, had violent mood swings and would also see imaginary people. We return to her story in Vignette 1.9, as told by her daughter.

Vignette 1.9 Vascular dementia: Joy's case as told by her daughter

My mother kept seeing imaginary people. She was so convincing that we used to go and check that there wasn't anyone there! When my sister died three years ago mum did not know who Berta was or that she was her daughter. The moment that I realised she no longer knew that I was her daughter, two years ago, was a terrible time for me. In the last two years that she lived with us, she needed 24-hour care –

she couldn't be left alone at all because she would either wander off or hurt herself, she never slept for more than 30 minutes at a time during the night. She became incontinent and incapable of doing anything for herself. Finally my husband and I realised that we could no longer provide her with the care that she needed and one year ago she went into a 'special' nursing home, or EMI (Elderly Mentally Infirm) Unit. Now she is unaware of who she is, what she is or where she is.

1.6.1 Signs and symptoms of vascular dementia

Similarly to Alzheimer's dementia, vascular dementia results in progressive impairment of the 'higher' (executive) functions of the brain such as working memory, new learning, recognition, fine motor movements and planning. Crucially, the distinction between vascular dementia and Alzheimer's dementia may be (at times) difficult, given the symptomatic overlap, but can be aided by the careful analysis and comparison of the following signs and symptoms of vascular dementia:

- an abrupt onset (e.g. following a stroke), whereas AD has a very slow onset
- stepped decline with symptoms remaining at a constant level and then suddenly deteriorating
- patchy cognitive impairments: for example, a significant memory impairment and a less significant deficit in language
- problems concentrating and communicating
- difficulties in planning, which may be more prominent than memory deficits
- focal neurological signs and symptoms: for example, symptoms of stroke, such as physical weakness or paralysis of an arm
- epileptic seizures
- wandering and getting lost (also likely in AD).

Individuals with vascular dementia may also experience mood swings and excessive emotional responses to trivial matters, often escalating into physical or verbal aggression. They may also show symptoms of depression (these are more common than in Alzheimer's dementia) and delusions and hallucinations (also more common than in Alzheimer's dementia). On the other hand, these people retain insight into their memory problems until the later stages, compared with Alzheimer's dementia where these types of insights are lost early on.

Vascular dementia is likely to produce both cognitive and non-cognitive symptoms and the former may be screened for using the MMSE. Major functional changes in people with this type of dementia are also usually picked up by the CDR and FAST.

1.6.2 Causes of vascular dementia

To be healthy and function properly, all cells in the brain need a good supply of blood, which carries oxygen and nutrients. Blood is delivered through a network of blood vessels called the vascular system (Figure 1.17). If the vascular system within the brain becomes damaged such that blood cannot reach brain cells, the cells will eventually die. This can lead to the onset of vascular dementia, which may manifest in different ways; either with:

- an abrupt onset, following a stroke
- a progressive decline following several mini-strokes in the cortex or in the inner parts of the brain, or
- a combination of both, a stroke and several mini-strokes.

What Joy may have actually experienced depends on which area of the brain had been damaged. If the area in question is responsible for movement of a limb, paralysis might occur. If it is responsible for speech, the person may develop problems speaking. Equally, damage to particular areas in the brain (such as the medial temporal lobes; see the case of HM in Section 1.3) can cause similar symptoms to Alzheimer's dementia. The strokes can be so small that the person might not notice any symptoms, or the symptoms may be only temporary. This is called multi-infarct dementia, caused by temporary interruptions in the blood supply within the brain, known as transient ischaemic attacks (or TIAs).

■ Joy's symptoms seem to be the result of which type of vascular dementia onset?

☐ Joy illustrates a case of progressive decline as a result of mini-strokes. By contrast, a stroke is likely to cause an *abrupt* onset which is generally accompanied by *sudden* and dramatic behavioural alterations.

What may cause damage to the vascular system in the brain?

The risk factors for vascular dementia are somewhat similar to those for stroke and heart disease. They include high blood pressure, atherosclerosis (narrowing of main arteries) in the neck supplying blood to the brain, raised cholesterol, diabetes, heart attacks (myocardial infarction and ischaemic heart disease) and smoking. Myocardial infarction is the interruption of blood supply to part of the heart causing heart cells to die. Ischaemic heart disease is characterised by reduced blood supply to the heart muscle.

Activity 1.4 Living with vascular dementia
(LO 1.3) Allow 30 minutes

Now would be a good time to go to the multimedia map and listen to the interview with Deborah who tells the story of her mother, who was diagnosed with vascular dementia.

1.6.3 Treatment, course and prognosis of vascular dementia

There is no cure for vascular dementia, and the brain damage that causes the dementia is usually very difficult to reverse. However, it may be possible to slow its progression in several ways. The health team's focus is currently on preventing further brain damage by improving blood circulation (for example, drugs that prevent the formation of blood clots may reduce risk of further strokes and improve circulation) and also through the prescription of medication to treat any underlying conditions, such as high blood pressure, high cholesterol, diabetes or heart problems.

In addition, individuals diagnosed with vascular dementia should consider adopting a healthier lifestyle by stopping smoking, taking regular exercise, eating healthily, and drinking alcohol only in moderation. Finally, people may benefit from receiving rehabilitative support, such as physiotherapy, occupational therapy and speech therapy, to help them maximise their opportunities to regain their lost functions.

The early detection and accurate diagnosis of vascular dementia are essential for enabling management and treatment of the condition. The course of vascular dementia varies considerably, depending on which part of the vascular system is affected. In the early stages, the person may only show memory problems and some difficulties with problem-solving and planning. The illness is associated with long periods of stability, interrupted by intermittent worsening. The progression of the illness also depends on the number, severity and control of the underlying vascular risk factors, as explained above. Overall, the duration of survival is similar to that for AD.

1.7 Final word

This chapter has introduced you to the three main types of dementia: Alzheimer's, frontotemporal and vascular dementia. The typical changes expected in each of these disorders have been illustrated with stories of different people's experiences, which convey a strong impression of how neurodegeneration brings about dramatic and irreversible cognitive and non-cognitive changes to those affected. Contrary to popular belief, dementia does not inevitably come with ageing. For example, the evidence suggests that only about one per 100 individuals will be affected by Alzheimer's dementia at the age of 65.

We have also explored different types of memory in order to understand how neurodegeneration in the medial temporal lobes and the hippocampus leads to impairment of semantic and episodic memories. Insight into the feeling of not having memory was illustrated by the case of HM who lost the ability to form new memories at the age of 27. The same, it seems, happens with people with Alzheimer's dementia who at some point cannot connect past, present and future events. We are, unfortunately, some way from finding a treatment to reverse the symptoms of dementia. Yet, scientists have clarified several aspects of the biological changes in Alzheimer's dementia, which will hopefully pave the way for new approaches towards the treatment of dementia. The biology of Alzheimer's dementia is the focus of the next chapter.

1.8 Summary of Chapter 1

- Dementia can be understood as a progressive disorder of the brain caused by neuronal degeneration and death, which leads to widespread changes in brain function.

- The main types of dementia are Alzheimer's dementia (affecting 2 in 3 people with dementia), frontotemporal dementia (affecting 1 in 50) and vascular dementia (affecting 1 in 4).

- Dementia changes the personalities, abilities and habits of people who, consequently, may become strangers to family members and friends. However, none of these dramatic changes will be under the individual's conscious control.

- Although not much is known about why individuals develop dementia, its onset seems to be influenced by a range of biological, social and environmental factors.

- Dementia does not come inevitably with ageing. Only approximately 1 in every 100 individuals aged 65–69 will be affected.

- Anterograde amnesia refers to the inability to form new memories after a trauma. Retrograde amnesia refers to loss of memory for events directly preceding a trauma.

- Declarative memory includes semantic memory, which concerns words, ideas, facts and information taken independent of context; and episodic memory, which concerns information that may be specific to particular contexts, such as a time and a place in a person's life. Both of these types of memory are processed in the medial temporal lobes and, specifically, the hippocampus.

- When diagnosing dementia, clinicians should rule out depressive disorders, delirium, mild or moderate mental retardation, premorbid states of subnormal cognitive functioning and mental disorders caused by medication.

- People with normal age-related cognitive loss and people with dementia differ in terms of the *range* of cognitive domains being affected and how *severely* each of the domains is affected. The former are likely to have subclinical impairments in one cognitive domain, usually memory, whereas the latter typically will show severe impairments in several cognitive and functional domains.

- Whereas AD typically affects the individual's memory abilities, frontotemporal dementia affects their emotional management, leading to isolation, anger and disinhibited behaviours. Vascular dementia, on the other hand, occurs as a result of impaired blood supply to the brain with variable consequences depending on the brain area affected.

- Amnestic MCI is seen by some as an intermediate stage between normal age-related memory loss and AD. Some studies suggest that nearly half of individuals with amnestic MCI develop dementia within a period of 48 months; others show that MCI may in many cases be reversible.

- Taken together, the evidence suggests that the current concept of amnestic MCI does not capture the full spectrum of the disorder. Because not all individuals with amnestic MCI will progress to overt AD, the identification and refinement of cognitive, genetic and biological markers that allow the definition and detection of an early stage of Alzheimer's dementia and the prediction of its course remains a clinical research priority.

1.9 Learning outcomes

LO 1.1 Explain the rates of prevalence and incidence of dementia. (KU1, CS1, KS1)

LO 1.2 Distinguish between different types of memory and describe the brain areas involved in memory. (KU2)

LO 1.3 Describe the signs and symptoms associated with Alzheimer's dementia, frontotemporal dementia and vascular dementia. (KU4)

LO 1.4 Describe the concepts of normal age-related memory decline and mild cognitive impairment. (KU4)

1.10 Self-assessment questions

SAQ 1.1 (LO 1.1)

If you were to calculate a healthy 80-year-old's chance of developing Alzheimer's dementia within the next year, where would you look for this type of information, and what is the estimated chance for that to happen?

SAQ 1.2 (LO 1.2)

Which areas of the brain appear to be involved in declarative memories?

SAQ 1.3 (LO 1.3)

The behaviour of people with frontotemporal dementia and Alzheimer's dementia will differ considerably, at least initially. What are the main differences?

SAQ 1.4 (LO 1.4)

Which essential argument (and evidence) has led some researchers to doubt the usefulness of amnestic MCI as a valid predictor of Alzheimer's dementia?

Chapter 2 The biology of Alzheimer's dementia

Katherine Leys

2.1 Introduction

In Book 1, Section 1.1.1, you were introduced to Mark, a 65-year-old man who has severe memory loss. Mark's family has accepted that he has some form of dementia which is caused by damage to parts of his brain. The progression of the condition appears to be inevitable and, although Mark is taking medication, this will at best slow down the rate of his decline. In contrast to some of the other mental health conditions described in Book 1, dementia is seen as primarily arising from changes in brain biology, rather than psychological or social factors. Nevertheless, the symptoms of dementia that you read about in the previous chapter of this book cannot all be explained by biology. For example, the loss of cognitive abilities caused by dementia may lead to social withdrawal and lack of stimulation, which may have additional psychological and physical effects. In a wider context, dementia has devastating psychological and social effects on the family members and friends involved in caring for the person with dementia.

The previous chapter described the experience and diagnosis of the main types of dementia. You read the story of Filip, who developed Alzheimer's dementia in his sixties, and the challenges faced by his family. Alzheimer's dementia (AD) or dementia of Alzheimer's type (DAT) is the most common form of dementia and will be the focus of this chapter. The chapter will focus on the underlying biology of AD and will attempt to relate the brain changes seen in AD to the symptoms of memory loss and cognitive decline. Over the last few decades, AD has been the subject of intense research leading to various theories of how it develops. You will see that the story is far from over: there are uncertainties and limitations to our current knowledge of the possible causes of AD and the progression of the condition.

- ■ Pause for a moment and think about why it is so important to carry out research into the biology of Alzheimer's dementia. How could the outcomes of this research be used?

- ☐ Understanding the biological changes in the brain may provide the basis for the development of future treatments, particularly drug therapies. It's also possible that this knowledge may lead to the development of preventive measures.

Book 1 also introduced the idea that genes affect the development of the brain (Section 1.2.3) and therefore the likelihood of the development of a mental illness during a person's lifetime. This chapter will consider the evidence for a genetic basis for AD, a subject that has attracted considerable media interest. The identification of genes associated with AD has advanced our understanding of how the condition develops and will perhaps lead to new areas of treatment or prevention.

A tissue is a collection of cells with similar structure and function.

The discussion will start with a review of the characteristic pathology or structural changes to the cells and tissues of the brain that are associated with AD.

2.2 Alzheimer's pathology

2.2.1 Investigating the pathology

As mentioned in Section 1.2.1, Alzheimer's dementia is named after a German psychiatrist, Alois Alzheimer, who performed an autopsy on a 51-year-old woman who had been experiencing deficiencies in memory and comprehension. Alzheimer described two types of abnormal deposits in the woman's brain. These were deposits of a dense, insoluble substance in the spaces between neurons, now known as **amyloid plaques** (also referred to as senile plaques) and twisted filamentous structures inside neurons, now called **neurofibrillary tangles** (Figure 2.1). These two features have become the defining pathological hallmarks of AD and they form the basis for the differentiation of AD from other forms of dementia.

It is now known that amyloid plaques consist primarily of a substance called **beta-amyloid** (β-amyloid, sometimes abbreviated to Aβ) and neurofibrillary tangles consist of a protein called tau. Sections 2.5 and 2.6 describe the production of β-amyloid and tau and the evidence for their contribution to the onset of the symptoms of AD, but first we will consider the structural and functional changes of the brain in more detail and how brain scanning is being used to study these changes.

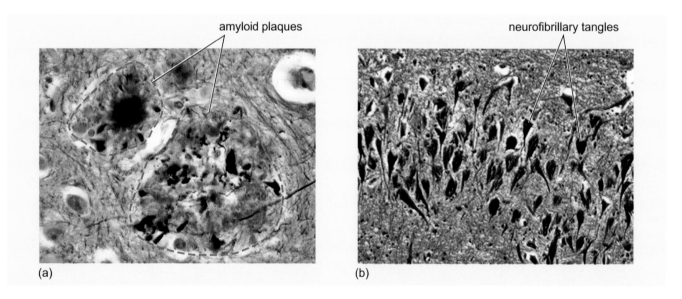

Figure 2.1 Photomicrographs showing (a) amyloid plaques and (b) neurofibrillary tangles in the brain of a person with Alzheimer's dementia. These deposits are mainly found in areas of the cerebral cortex and the hippocampus.

Activity 2.1 Brain deposits in Alzheimer's dementia

(LO 2.1) Allow 30 minutes

Now would be a good time to examine the photomicrographs of AD brain tissue in the multimedia map and answer the questions associated with the activity.

As well as the brain deposits of amyloid and tau, post-mortem examination shows that AD is associated with severe loss of brain volume in several areas, as mentioned in Book 1, Section 2.2.1, and the previous chapter of this book. This loss of volume is most evident in parts of the cerebral cortex, the outer layer of the cerebral hemispheres. The cerebral cortex is divided into four areas, or lobes, and it has a large surface area due to its many folds and ridges (Figure 2.2). Examination of brains from people with advanced AD shows shrinkage of the frontal and temporal lobes of the cortex, enlargement of spaces between areas and a loss of surface area (Figure 2.3).

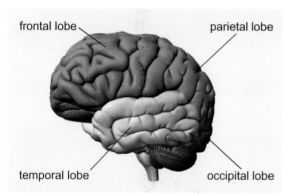

Figure 2.2 Diagram of the cerebral cortex showing the location of the four lobes.

Until recently, it has only been possible to identify the abnormal deposits of AD by the examination of brain tissue, and therefore a definitive diagnosis based on the pathology has only been possible after death. As discussed in Chapter 1, clinicians may arrive at a probable diagnosis of AD based on the results of an assessment such as the MMSE, supplemented with a brain scan showing brain atrophy. But recent advances in neuroimaging techniques have enabled accurate investigation of specific brain changes associated with AD and, as you will see, some types of brain scan allow the identification in the living brain of some of the deposits described above. These techniques are changing the way that AD is diagnosed and will be particularly useful in the mild to moderate stages. It may soon be possible to offer people worried about memory loss a definitive answer to their question of whether they are in the early stages of AD.

The discussion will now turn to the techniques of MRI, fMRI and PET and how they are being used to further our knowledge of the development of AD.

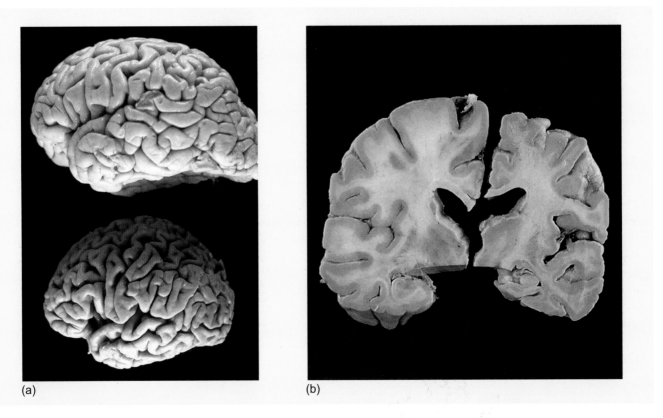

(a) (b)

Figure 2.3 (a) Side view of a brain from a healthy person (top) compared with a brain from a person with Alzheimer's dementia, showing that AD causes considerable shrinkage of the brain. The front of each brain is towards the left. The frontal and temporal lobes in particular are reduced in size in AD and the gaps (sulci) between the ridges are wider, showing loss of cortical volume. (b) Sections from a healthy brain on the left of the figure and from a brain of a person with AD on the right of the figure.

You have encountered these techniques in previous books, but Box 2.1 provides a brief summary of how they work.

Box 2.1 Summary of some of the brain imaging techniques used in the study of Alzheimer's dementia

MRI (magnetic resonance imaging)

MRI uses a strong magnetic field to detect different tissues or components of the brain. It relies on the fact that atoms respond to the magnetic field and emit energy which is detected by the sensors around the head. MRI scans detect energy emitted by hydrogen atoms and convert this into a detailed image of the structure of the brain. Different areas of the brain have slightly different compositions, and those areas with higher levels of hydrogen atoms appear brighter in the image than those with lower levels of hydrogen atoms. Scans can be taken at various orientations of the head, therefore providing images of different cross-sections of the brain.

fMRI (functional magnetic resonance imaging)

fMRI is a version of MRI that can detect activity in the brain rather than structure alone. It detects oxygen levels (in the form of oxyhaemoglobin; see Book 2, Box 4.3) in the brain before and during a task. The areas with the greatest changes in oxygen levels indicate the areas that are active during the task, as brain activity results in an increase in oxygen delivery via the blood supply. The difference in oxygen levels is converted to a coloured scale and the resulting image shows the areas where the activity is the most intense.

PET (positron emission tomography)

PET works by detecting particles emitted by a radioactive substance which is given to the participant by injection before the scanning procedure. In some cases, a radioactive substance is used which binds to certain structures in the brain in order to show the location of these structures. In the example in Section 2.2.1, a substance is used which binds to β-amyloid. In other cases, PET can be used to show activity in the brain during a particular task. This involves the use of radioactive substances that are taken up by the brain during the task in order to show the areas of the brain that are most active during the task (Book 3, Box 2.2).

MRI

MRI scans of people with AD show atrophy (shrinkage) in the cortex, particularly in the temporal lobes, and the hippocampus (Figure 2.4). (The role of the hippocampus in memory formation was described in Section 1.3.) It is possible to measure the volume of brain areas with some accuracy using MRI, leading to the possibility that the technique could be used in early diagnosis. A recent large multisite study using MRI has demonstrated that hippocampal volume is lower in people with AD compared with people with mild cognitive impairment and age-matched people with normal cognition scores. The study also demonstrated that there was a greater loss of hippocampal volume over 12 months in people with AD than either of the control groups, and that the rate of loss of volume correlated with the rate of loss of cognition (Schuff et al., 2009). The authors of this report suggest that hippocampal volume measured using MRI is a useful indicator of AD pathology and can be used to track brain changes over time.

A multisite or multicentre study involves the recruitment of large numbers of participants and uses several research centres. In the example here, around 50 research centres were used to perform the scans and cognitive assessments on around 400 participants throughout the USA and Canada.

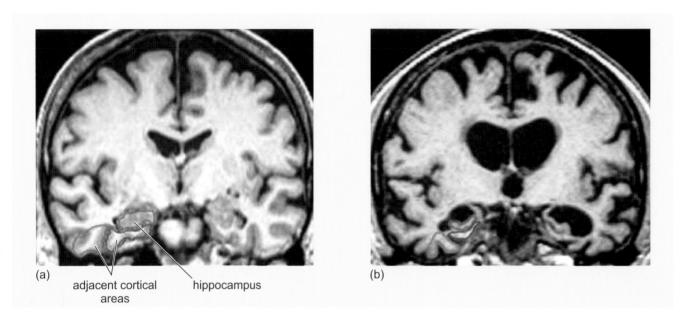

Figure 2.4 MRI scans of (a) normal and (b) AD brains, showing loss of cortical volume and enlarged spaces in AD, particularly in the hippocampus and adjacent cortical areas of the temporal lobe.

fMRI

Functional MRI scans have an advantage over MRI in that they can be used to measure activity in the brain as well as structure. This technique has been used to study the brain areas active during memory performance tasks in order to understand how the function of the brain is altered in AD compared with normal ageing (Figure 2.5).

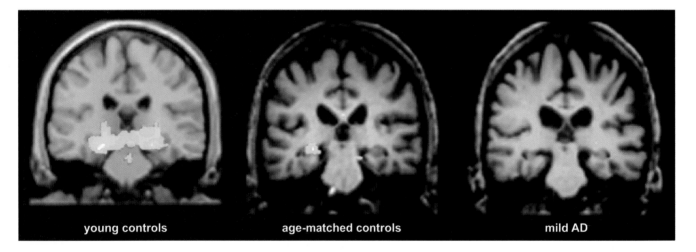

Figure 2.5 fMRI scans from young control participants, age-matched control participants and participants with mild AD (mean MMSE rating 22.6) during a memory task. Areas of activation are shown in yellow. Average activity for each group of participants is shown on a representative structural image from each group. Both young and age-matched controls showed activation in the hippocampus, although the activation was greater in extent in the young controls. Participants with mild AD showed no activation in the hippocampus.

In the study illustrated in Figure 2.5, participants with mild AD were compared with control participants in a series of face–name recognition tasks, which involved memorising the names of people in a series of photographs (Sperling et al., 2003). As the figure shows, there was a decrease in activity in the hippocampus in mild AD compared with the age-matched controls. The results could not entirely be explained by hippocampal atrophy in the AD participants. This suggests some hippocampal dysfunction in early AD. It is suggested that fMRI is useful in assessing patterns of brain activation early in the course of AD and to distinguish changes seen in AD from those seen with normal ageing.

PET

The ability to measure structural and functional changes in AD such as those described above is a great step forward. However, the ultimate goal is to detect the characteristic brain deposits associated with AD without having to wait for an autopsy. In the last few years some researchers have managed to do just that (Mathis et al., 2005). Chemicals have been developed that bind to β-amyloid, the main constituent of amyloid plaques. Participants are given a radioactive form of this chemical and a PET scan is performed to show the distribution and levels of β-amyloid in the brain. Figure 2.6 shows the widespread distribution of β-amyloid in the cortex of a person with AD compared with very low levels of this deposit in the cortex of a healthy control. Some of the people with AD who have taken part in these studies have since died and it has been possible to compare their post-mortem brains with the results of the PET scans. A close correlation has been seen between the β-amyloid deposits detected by PET and the amyloid plaques seen at post-mortem, showing that the scanning technique gives an accurate measure during life of the brain deposits previously only visible after death (Hoffman and Froemke, 2009). Clearly this technique offers clinicians a good diagnostic tool based on Alzheimer's pathology to be used alongside other diagnostic criteria. It also opens up a whole new area of research into the pathology of AD and linking the pathology to the symptoms that occur in this condition.

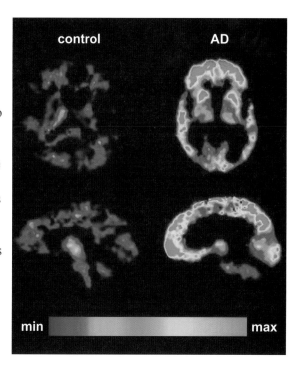

Figure 2.6 PET scans from a person with AD and a healthy control participant after injection of a radioactive chemical that binds to β-amyloid. The coloured scale indicates the level of amyloid deposition from low (blue) to high (red).

- This section has discussed the use of brain imaging to detect and measure the pathological changes associated with Alzheimer's dementia. Can you think of any potential advantages to people with AD arising from this area of research?

- A definitive diagnosis of AD in the initial stages of the condition has already been mentioned; this allows the possibility of starting appropriate treatment at an earlier stage. You may also have thought of the possibility of testing people for the presence of AD before the onset of symptoms, tracking the progression of the condition or monitoring the effectiveness of various treatments.

2.2.2 Linking damage to disorder

The previous section describes how people with Alzheimer's dementia have widespread damage throughout the brain, including the loss of areas of the cortex and hippocampus and the formation of abnormal deposits. How can this damage explain the symptoms of memory loss and cognitive decline seen in AD?

The study of people without dementia, but with damage to areas of the brain associated with memory deficits, has provided a wealth of information about the function of various areas. A very famous example already mentioned in Section 1.3 is that of HM who had an area of his temporal lobe and surrounding tissue, including his hippocampus, removed in an attempt to cure his epilepsy. After surgery, HM was unable to form any new declarative memories, in other words memories of events or new information. His procedural memory, in other words his ability to learn how to perform new tasks, was not damaged. The cases of HM and other individuals have shown that the hippocampus plays a crucial role in some types of memory formation. Other studies have shown the importance of cortical association areas in the storage and retrieval of memories.

Cortical association areas are areas of the cortex that are involved in the higher or advanced stages of information processing.

The cortex has many other complex functions, including the processing and integration of sensory information, planning motor activity, linking information to emotional states and feelings, and production of speech and language. At a simplistic level then, it is not surprising that the damage or loss of cortical areas causes the decline of many cognitive functions. Many of the drugs that have been developed to treat this aspect of AD act on cortical regions, and these are discussed in Chapter 3.

The next section delves a little bit deeper into the pathology of AD at the level of neurons and neurotransmitters and describes the research leading to one of the most accepted explanations for the onset of AD.

2.3 The cholinergic hypothesis

2.3.1 The role of acetylcholine in the brain

Acetylcholine is one of the most widespread neurotransmitters in the brain and it acts mainly in an excitatory way; that is, it increases the chances of an action potential occurring in a neighbouring neuron. Neurons that release acetylcholine are known as **cholinergic neurons** (Book 3, Figure 2.10). Cell bodies of cholinergic neurons are found in particular abundance in an area of the brainstem called the pons, and in a group of structures near the front of the brain known as the basal forebrain. Axons from these cell bodies extend to several areas of the brain and therefore are implicated in many functions. Figure 2.7 shows the pathways of cholinergic axons to various areas throughout the brain including the hippocampus and cortex.

■ Whereabouts in the pathways shown in Figure 2.7 will acetylcholine be released and have an effect on other neurons?

□   It will be released at the end of the pathways, from the axon terminals. Therefore it will act on the areas at the end of the pathways: for example, it will have an effect on the neurons in the hippocampus.

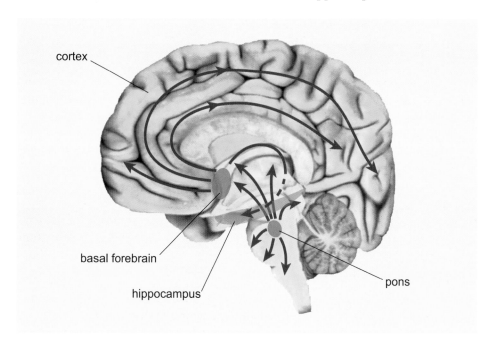

Figure 2.7 Diagram of the brain showing the location of the main cholinergic pathways.

2.3.2 The development of the hypothesis

Evidence started to build up from the 1970s onwards that loss of acetylcholine may be implicated in the development of AD symptoms. The initial line of evidence came from clinical reports that **cholinergic receptor antagonists** interfere with various memory tasks and cognitive performance, even in young patients.

■   What is a receptor antagonist?

□   A chemical that blocks the activation of receptors by the neurotransmitter, such that the administration of an antagonist would have the same effect as a reduced level of neurotransmitter.

Since these early reports, many studies with cholinergic antagonists have been performed in non-human species, such as rodents, which have confirmed the role of acetylcholine in learning and memory. Indeed, the use of non-human species injected with cholinergic antagonists has been developed into a useful research tool for AD, which you will learn more about in the next section.

The second line of evidence for the involvement of the cholinergic system in AD was provided by experiments performed on post-mortem brains of people with AD. These experiments measured factors relating to cholinergic activity: for example, enzymes involved in the synthesis or breakdown of acetylcholine, or levels of cholinergic receptors. One of the most widely studied of these factors is the enzyme that synthesises acetylcholine, **choline acetyltransferase (ChAT)**. The presence of ChAT in a certain area of the brain implies the presence of cholinergic neurons, since neurotransmitters are synthesised inside the neuronal cell body.

■ Remind yourself of the cholinergic pathways shown in Figure 2.7. What would a reduction in ChAT levels in the basal forebrain mean in terms of cholinergic activity in the brain?

□ It would imply that cholinergic neurons in the basal forebrain are damaged or lost. There will therefore be less acetylcholine released in the areas that the basal forebrain neurons extend to and so less activation of acetylcholine receptors in those areas.

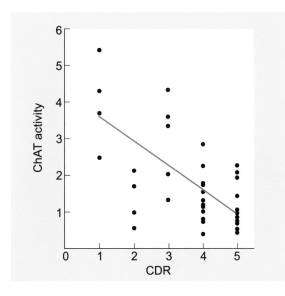

Figure 2.8 Graph showing the relationship between ChAT activity in post-mortem brain samples from people with AD and severity of symptoms on the CDR scale (Section 1.4.3; 1 = mild, 2 = moderate, 3 = severe, 4 = profound and 5 = terminal). The units for measuring ChAT activity are complex and have been left out. The correlation between the two variables was shown in a statistical test to be significant.

Many studies have shown a reduction in ChAT levels in various areas of the brain of people with AD and some studies report a correlation between ChAT levels after death and the severity of symptoms before death (Perry, 1986; Bierer et al., 1995) (Figure 2.8). It is generally the consensus that these and other studies are consistent with a reduction in the numbers of cholinergic neurons in the AD brain. However, it must be remembered that most of these studies have been done with brains from people in the end stages of AD, so the significance of these changes in the progression of the condition is unclear. Furthermore, it has also been demonstrated that there is a decline in the number of cholinergic neurons in normal ageing and in other conditions with dementia such as Parkinson's disease.

■ What type of correlation is shown in the graph in Figure 2.8?

□ This is a negative correlation, in which the level of one variable decreases as the other variable increases (Book 1, Box 4.5).

■ Why should you be cautious in interpreting the results of correlations?

□ A correlation does not necessarily mean that one factor is caused by the other, or vice versa. There may be another explanation: for example, that a third factor causes both of the factors measured.

Despite the uncertainties, the experiments and observations described above led to the development in the early 1980s of the 'cholinergic hypothesis' to explain the symptoms of memory and cognitive decline seen in AD. The hypothesis states that the decline of cognitive function in AD is due to a degeneration or loss of cholinergic neurons in the brain, particularly in the basal forebrain, beyond that expected in normal ageing. Not surprisingly, this hypothesis led to the use of various drugs that target the cholinergic system as possible therapies for AD, which you will read more about in the next chapter.

Research has moved on, but it remains accepted that a loss of cholinergic neurons occurs in AD, at least in the advanced stages, and that there is a link between the cholinergic system and the pathogenic events of AD (Auld et al., 2002; Schliebs and Arendt, 2006). Sections 2.5 and 2.6 will examine these events in more detail in an attempt to unravel the order of events that lead to the symptoms of AD. But before that, the next section provides a brief overview of research using non-human species, which has contributed enormously to our understanding of this type of dementia.

2.4 Animal models of cognition

2.4.1 Developing a model

Researching the biological basis of any brain disorder in humans is difficult. Analysis of brain tissue is possible after death, but this tells us little about the early stages or the progression of the disorder. Brain scanning techniques are developing rapidly, but the information provided about cells, proteins and neurotransmitters is currently limited. Observation of human behaviour in tightly controlled environments is not possible, neither is it acceptable to administer drugs to humans that may cause harm. Full-scale controlled trials in humans are carried out to assess possible drug treatments, but these are time-consuming and costly to organise, and can only be carried out after extensive testing in non-human species. For all of these reasons, the establishment of a valid animal model for AD is seen as essential in gaining a greater understanding of the condition and to assess possible drug therapies. An animal model is the use of a non-human species to gain insight into humans (Book 2, Box 2.4 and Book 3, Section 1.3.1). In the context of AD, the animal should exhibit similar symptoms to those seen in the human condition. There are various ways of engineering these models and the ones used the most extensively in AD research are summarised in Box 2.2.

Box 2.2 Modelling Alzheimer's dementia in non-human species

Pharmacological models involve the administration of a drug that has a known effect. Many researchers have used rats and monkeys injected with cholinergic antagonists as models for AD, following earlier reports that these substances cause memory deficits. In this type of model, the concentration of drug can be altered and therefore dose-dependent effects can be investigated. A problem with the technique is that acetylcholine is a widespread neurotransmitter in the brain and therefore many processes and behaviours are disrupted by the antagonists.

Lesion models involve a **lesion** or destruction of an area of brain tissue. Lesions can be formed in various ways such as surgically (cutting a neuronal pathway or removing a piece of tissue), electrically (destruction of cells or tissue with an electric current delivered by a microelectrode)

---

or chemically (destruction of tissue by injection of a toxin which can be specific to certain types of cell). An example of a lesion model used in AD is the chemical destruction of cholinergic neurons in the basal forebrain of rats.

Genetic models involve either removing or inactivating genes, or adding genes to one animal from another animal of a different species. When a gene is added to an animal in this way, the animal is said to be **transgenic**. Certain types of AD have been found to have a genetic basis (described in Section 2.9) and some of these genes have been identified and incorporated into mouse cells, thus giving rise to mouse transgenic models for AD. It has been found that these mice develop some of the characteristic pathology of AD, including amyloid plaques.

Activity 2.2 Benefits and drawbacks of animal models
(LOs 2.3 and 2.5) Allow 15 minutes

An advantage and a disadvantage of pharmacological models of Alzheimer's dementia are mentioned in Box 2.2. Make a list of possible benefits and drawbacks associated with lesion models and genetic models of AD.

2.4.2 Finding a suitable measure

When developing animal models for Alzheimer's dementia, researchers must consider the cognitive impairments in AD and how to identify an equivalent impairment in a non-human species that can be measured accurately. Section 1.4 described the main changes reported in AD, which include problems with memory and learning, complex reasoning, attention, orientation, motor performance, speech and language. Clearly, speech and language is impossible to model in a laboratory rat! Most animal models have focused on tasks that involve learning and/or memory, or spatial coordination, but this is difficult to define precisely. For example, a task involving the learning of a route through a maze could involve motivation (to find food, for example), attention, motor performance and orientation, as well as learning and memory. However, an attempt is made to refine and manipulate the tasks in various ways so that the behaviour reflects different brain processes.

A well-established method of assessing learning and memory in rats is to use a tank of water with a submerged platform, known as a Morris water maze (Figure 2.9a). The water is cloudy so that the rat cannot see the platform. When the rat is placed in the tank for the first time, it swims around the tank to find a way out and when it finds the platform it climbs onto it. In subsequent trials, the rat learns to find the quickest route to the platform by remembering the location of the platform relative to features located around the room. The rat forms a spatial map of its environment and uses it to navigate its way around the tank.

Another effective way of testing memory in rodents is to use a radial maze with eight 'arms' leading from a central area (Figure 2.9b). Some or all of the arms have a piece of food at the end. In order to obtain all the food, the animal must remember which arms it has previously visited. There are many other variations of mazes that have been used with rats and mice, usually involving a task that must be learned in order to receive a reward of some kind. The strength of these methods is that they are cognitively demanding; in other words, the rodent has to acquire complex information about its world in order to solve the task.

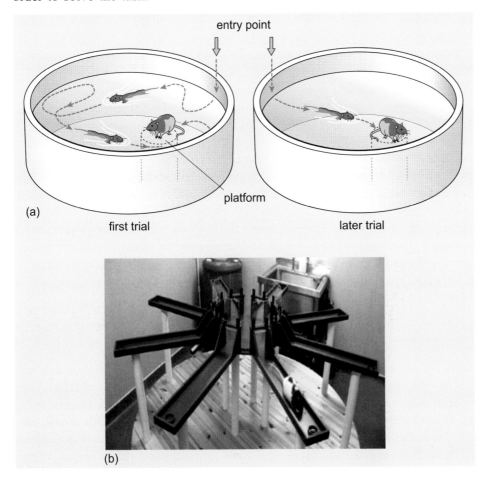

Figure 2.9 (a) Diagram of a Morris water maze and (b) photograph of a radial maze.

Activity 2.3 Radial maze

(LO 2.3) Allow 40 minutes

Now would be a good time to watch the film clip showing the use of a radial maze in the multimedia map. You will see trained rats using the radial maze and be able to count the number of errors made by individual rats. There are also some questions linked to the activity.

More sophisticated types of cognitive ability test can be performed on monkeys: for example, tasks that require discrimination between objects or matching of objects. However, rodents remain the most commonly used species for most animal models.

Figure 2.10 shows the results of an experiment using a rat model for AD (Wang and Tang, 1998). In this experiment, the rats were injected with a cholinergic antagonist, scopolamine, and memory was assessed using a radial maze. The maze was partially baited; in other words, only four of the eight arms contained food (much like the maze task in Activity 2.3). Prior to treatment, the rats were trained to remember which of the arms contained the food. The baiting pattern was different for each rat to prevent the effect of odour cues or directional preferences within the maze. After treatment, the number of errors were recorded and classified into two different types. The first type of error was considered a working memory error and this was recorded when the rat re-entered a baited arm after consumption of the food. The second type was a classified by the researchers as a 'reference' memory error, which was recorded when the rat entered an unbaited arm. The results showed that scopolamine increased the number of both working and reference memory errors compared with control rats, which were treated with saline. The model was also used to assess the effects of various drugs on these memory impairments, thus providing a useful screening process for the use of potential treatments in humans. The reality of the effects of drugs in humans is, however, a more complex story than suggested by these experiments, as discussed in Chapter 3.

■ From the graphs in Figure 2.10, which of the three drugs appears to be the most effective in reversing the memory deficits caused by scopolamine?

☐ Drug 1 appears to be the most effective, as the number of working memory errors is reduced the most with this drug and it is effective at lower concentrations than the other two drugs. Drug 3 may be marginally more effective at reducing reference memory errors, but at a much higher dose than drug 1.

The results in Figure 2.10 are shown as means and SEMs, which are explained in Book 2, Box 1.3.

■ From Figure 2.10a, assuming an equal number of rats in each group, which of the groups produced the smallest spread of data around the mean?

☐ The saline-treated rats, as shown by the size of the bar above the mean value.

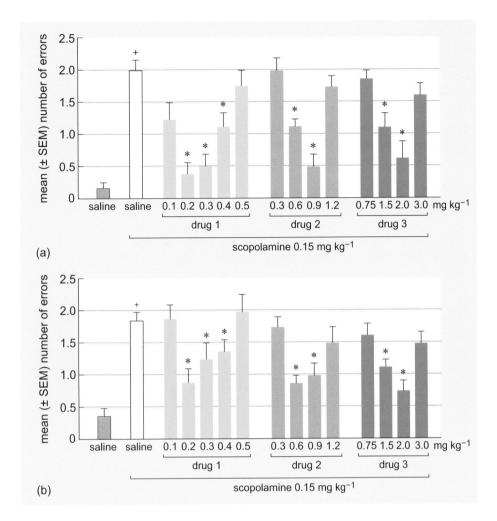

(a)

(b)

Figure 2.10 Graphs showing the effects of scopolamine on (a) working and (b) reference memory in rats, compared with the effects of administration of saline. The crosses show a statistical difference between the effects of scopolamine treatment and the effects of saline treatment. The graphs also show the effects of three different drugs on the scopolamine-induced memory impairments. The asterisks show where the drug had a statistically significant effect.

To summarise the story so far in this chapter, there are three characteristic features of AD: the loss of neurons in some areas of the brain including the cortex and hippocampus; deposits of β-amyloid; and deposits of tau. Brain scanning techniques such as MRI, fMRI and PET have allowed researchers to study some of the structural and functional changes associated with AD. Evidence from experiments, including those using animal models, has suggested that the cholinergic system is implicated in some of the symptoms of AD and that cholinergic neurons may be lost as the condition progresses. This has led to the development of treatments targeting the cholinergic system. The next two sections consider in more detail the biological processes behind the production of β-amyloid and tau and how these deposits may contribute to the development of AD symptoms.

2.5 Amyloid deposits

2.5.1 The amyloid peptide

Before reading this section, it may be worth your while reminding yourself of some of the features of neurons and synapses: for example, see Book 1, Section 2.3 and Activity 2.2. Knowledge of these biological processes is essential for fully understanding the brain changes in Alzheimer's dementia and the rationale behind various treatment strategies.

This section will start by describing how β-amyloid, the main component of amyloid plaques, is produced from neurons. β-amyloid is a **peptide**, which is a short portion of a protein composed of a chain of amino acids. Peptides are produced in cells as an intermediate form in the process of forming a protein, or alternatively they are produced by breaking down existing proteins. Proteins are broken down into peptides by the action of enzymes. Many peptides play an important role in the functioning of cells.

The β-amyloid peptide is formed from a protein known as the **amyloid precursor protein (APP)** by the action of enzymes called **secretases**. APP and the secretases are embedded in the neuronal cell membrane. It is thought that APP and its breakdown products play a role in the normal functioning of neurons, although it is not entirely clear what these functions might be. It is now believed, however, that β-amyloid plays a crucial role in the development of AD.

There are two different pathways involved in the breakdown of APP and these are described below.

Cell membranes surround all cells and provide a protective barrier between the inside of the cell and the extracellular fluid. They also control the movement of substances into and out of the cell. They contain many proteins that are essential for the functioning of the cell: for example, receptors and enzymes.

Non-amyloidogenic pathway

As its name suggests, this is a pathway that does not result in the production of β-amyloid. There are two secretases involved in this pathway, known as alpha-secretase (α-secretase) and gamma-secretase (γ-secretase). Figure 2.11a shows the sequence of events in the pathway. The first step is that α-secretase cuts APP at a position near the outside of the membrane, resulting in two fragments. One is released to the outside of the neuron, and the other remains embedded in the membrane. Then, the fragment in the membrane is cut by γ-secretase, resulting in two smaller pieces. None of the fragments formed in this pathway is thought to be harmful to neurons.

Amyloidogenic pathway

This pathway involves an additional secretase known as beta-secretase (β-secretase) and results in the production of β-amyloid. The first step is that β-secretase cuts APP at a different position to the one cut by α-secretase. The second step is that γ-secretase cuts the remaining fragment of APP as before. The small portion released from the middle of APP is the β-amyloid peptide. This sequence of events is illustrated in Figure 2.11b.

The sequence of events in both pathways is normal and happens in every one of us. The question is, what goes wrong in the brains of people with AD and

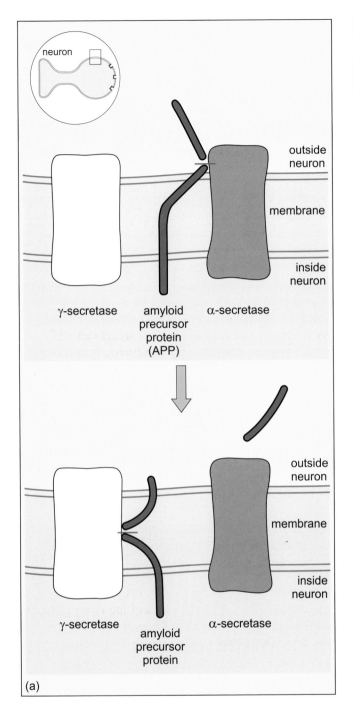

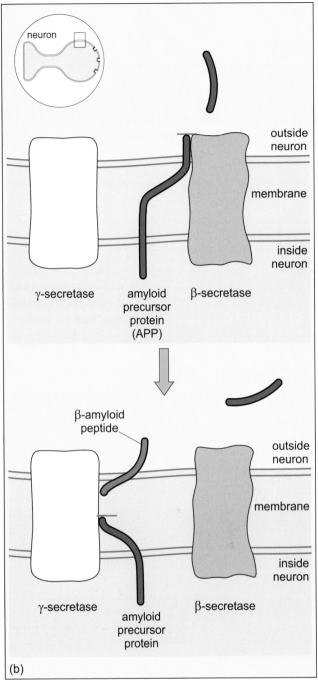

Figure 2.11 (a) The non-amyloidogenic pathway and (b) the amyloidogenic pathway of APP breakdown by secretases. β-amyloid peptide is formed during the latter pathway.

why do they contain plaques made up of large amounts of the β-amyloid peptide?

■ Can you suggest what processes could result in an increased production of β-amyloid?

□ Increased activity of β-secretase or decreased activity of α-secretase could increase the amyloidogenic pathway relative to the non-amyloidogenic pathway, thus increasing the amount of β-amyloid produced.

It appears that in normal brains the amount of β-amyloid produced is appropriate to fulfil its role and that levels are kept in check by controlling the amount produced and removing it as necessary. In people with AD, there is either too much produced or it is not removed effectively. The consequences of this are explored in the next section.

The story now gets more complex, as the β-amyloid peptide can vary slightly in length, from 39 to 43 amino acids long (Brouwers et al., 2008), depending on where the γ-secretase cuts the APP molecule. Usually, the main form of the β-amyloid peptide produced is 40 amino acids long, and there is a small proportion of a slightly longer peptide of 42 amino acids. The longer version of the peptide has a greater tendency to fold up into clumps, or aggregates, than the shorter version and is the predominant peptide found in amyloid plaques. The implication is that, under normal conditions, the longer form of β-amyloid is removed before it has a chance to accumulate in the brain.

Before moving on, it's worth mentioning that understanding the above two pathways has led to new ideas for treatments based on manipulating the action of the various secretases. These will be discussed in Chapter 3.

2.5.2 Formation of plaques and deposits

As mentioned in the previous section, β-amyloid has the tendency to form clumps within the spaces between neurons. If there is an excessive amount of the peptide present, the individual peptide molecules join together, firstly into small groups composed of a few peptides, called **oligomers**, and then into larger structures called **fibrils**. The fibrils are insoluble and eventually form into the large plaques that are characteristic of Alzheimer's dementia. These plaques are particularly prevalent throughout the cortex and hippocampus of people with AD.

Activity 2.4 Production of β-amyloid
(LOs 2.1 and 2.4) Allow 20 minutes

Now would be a good time to watch the animation on β-amyloid production and plaque formation in the multimedia map and answer the questions that follow.

How does the presence of amyloid plaques in AD relate to the loss of cholinergic neurons and the cholinergic hypothesis discussed in Section 2.3? Which of these pathologies occurs first in the development of the condition? Does one of them cause the other? Are they important in the development of symptoms or are they merely by-products of some other type of damage? These questions remain to some extent unanswered, but a huge research effort has taken place over the last two decades to investigate the role of β-amyloid in AD and will no doubt continue for some years to come. This chapter only has the space to skim the surface of the research in this area.

From the early 1990s onwards, various lines of evidence led scientists to propose an **amyloid cascade hypothesis**, which suggests that β-amyloid is produced in large quantities in AD and plays a central role in the development of symptoms (Selkoe, 1994). The original amyloid cascade hypothesis was that an excess amount of β-amyloid leads to the formation of plaques, which in turn leads to neuron death and ultimately the symptoms of memory loss seen in AD (Figure 2.12). However, there are some problems with this hypothesis: for example, there does not seem to be a clear correlation between the amount of amyloid plaque formation and the symptoms of AD (Tanzi, 2005). Further, amyloid plaques are sometimes found in normal ageing in the absence of AD (Whalley et al., 2004).

■   What sort of evidence would you look for to support the hypothesis that β-amyloid is involved in the development of AD pathology?

☐   You might look for evidence that β-amyloid has toxic effects on neurons consistent with the loss of neurons seen in the brains of people with AD. You could also investigate the possibility that β-amyloid causes some of the symptoms of AD or conversely, that blocking the production of β-amyloid slows down the development of these symptoms.

The next section will look briefly at some of this evidence.

2.5.3 The effect of β-amyloid on neurons

Many of the studies into the effect of β-amyloid on neurons have been performed using neuronal **cell cultures** (see Box 2.3). The advantage of these techniques is that the environment can be controlled precisely and effects of different substances on the activity of neurons can be measured. The obvious disadvantage is that the experiments do not represent the normal situation in the intact brain. Nonetheless, this type of study has shown that β-amyloid has several effects on cholinergic neurons, including disruption of acetylcholine release, reduction of acetylcholine levels inside the neuron, decreased glucose uptake and impaired receptor activation (Auld et al., 2002).

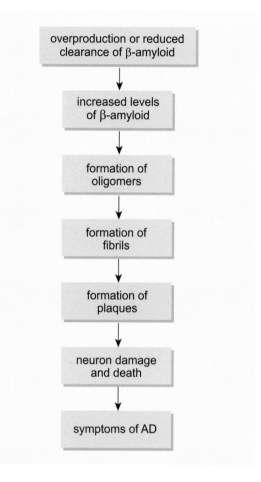

Figure 2.12 The original amyloid cascade hypothesis, in which overproduction or reduced clearance of β-amyloid leads to the formation of plaques and consequently damage to neurons.

Box 2.3 Cell culture

Cell culture experiments are performed using cells extracted from living organisms and kept alive and functioning in laboratory vessels. Sometimes small quantities of tissue can be used in the same way and these are referred to as tissue cultures. Cell or tissue cultures are very useful in investigating cellular or molecular mechanisms that cannot easily be investigated in an intact animal. They also have the advantage that large amounts of cells can be extracted from one animal, therefore reducing the number of animals needed for research. The cells or tissue can also sometimes be derived from humans.

The cells or tissues are kept at controlled temperatures and surrounded by fluid with the correct composition and nutrients necessary for survival and function. Substances can be added to the fluid in different concentrations in order to measure an effect. Sometimes cell lines can be developed in which the cells keep dividing and functioning for long periods of time. Some established cell lines have been used in laboratories round the world for many years.

The results of cell culture experiments should, however, be interpreted with caution. Cells sometimes lose their shape or structure when isolated from their usual surrounding support networks. They may also function differently when they are not part of an integrated system. Many cell lines are derived from tumours as they continue replicating indefinitely, but these cells may behave differently to non-tumour cells. Finally, some cell lines are derived from fetal tissue as these tend to survive better in culture, but this clearly raises ethical issues.

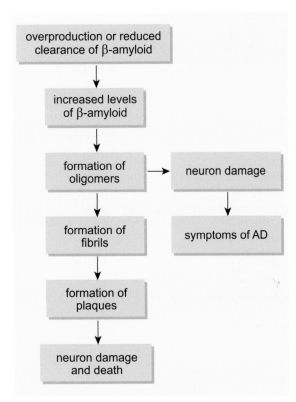

Figure 2.13 The revised amyloid cascade hypothesis, in which small soluble aggregates (oligomers) of β-amyloid cause neuronal dysfunction and memory loss.

Further experiments have shown that β-amyloid is toxic to neurons, causing degeneration and ultimately death of the neurons, but only after aggregation of β-amyloid has taken place (Klein, 2006), lending support to the amyloid cascade hypothesis.

Other studies, however, using transgenic mouse models of AD (Box 2.2), in which the mice produce high levels of β-amyloid, have shown that the mice have impaired memory *before* plaque formation and neuronal loss is evident (Dineley, 2007). These findings imply that another form of β-amyloid is responsible for the onset of AD symptoms, prior to the formation of plaques and neuron death. Evidence has accumulated in recent years that the soluble amyloid oligomers may be the initial cause of the symptoms of AD. For example, injection of amyloid oligomers into mice caused deficits in memory and learning (Dineley, 2007).

So, where does that leave us in terms of the amyloid cascade hypothesis of AD? Recent revisions of the hypothesis suggest that the main culprits for the development of symptoms are the small, soluble amyloid oligomers rather than the large, insoluble fibrils or plaques. Figure 2.13 shows a revised version of the amyloid cascade hypothesis, indicating that symptoms such as memory loss could occur before the formation of plaques and loss of neurons.

2.5.4 Synaptic dysfunction

The previous section discussed the possibility that amyloid oligomers are the initial cause of neuron dysfunction, leading to memory impairment and other symptoms seen in Alzheimer's dementia. Section 2.3 discussed the involvement of cholinergic neurons in memory, but so far the discussion has not considered the basis of memory formation in the brain at the cellular level. In fact, the synapse is crucial in learning and the formation of memory. A process called synaptic plasticity enables the formation of memory, by altering the structure of the synapse and increasing its efficiency. What is really interesting is that amyloid oligomers appear to disrupt this process of synaptic modification and therefore the formation of memory (Klein, 2006). These findings perhaps give an idea of the events in the brain in the initial stages of AD, where an increased level of oligomers could interfere with synaptic function and thus cause the initial symptoms of memory loss and inability to learn new tasks (Figure 2.14). It is an intriguing possibility that a therapeutic strategy could be developed to reverse the effects of the oligomers if the condition was detected at an early stage.

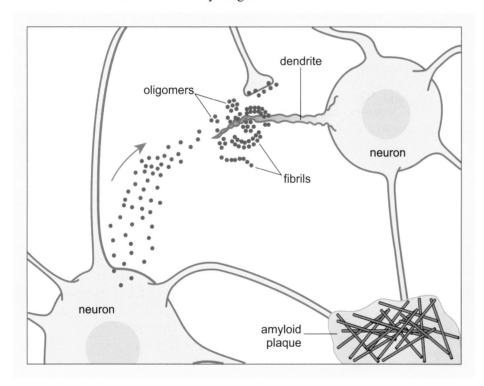

Figure 2.14 Illustration of the effect of amyloid oligomers on the synapses of neurons. The damage to synapses by oligomers probably occurs before the formation of amyloid fibrils and plaques. (Source: adapted from Gladstone Institutes, 2010)

■   Can you think of how any potential therapies might work in reducing the effects of amyloid oligomers on memory?

☐ You could target the oligomers themselves, either by removing them or reducing the amount produced; or you could interfere with the effects of oligomers at synapses if the specific target of the oligomers is identified.

The first strategy is quite difficult to achieve, although the use of secretase inhibitors (substances that inhibit the action of secretases; see Section 2.5.1) to reduce the amount of β-amyloid produced is currently being investigated. The use of a vaccine to reduce β-amyloid levels is also the subject of many current research studies. Both of these possibilities are discussed in the next chapter. What about the second strategy? Is it known exactly how the oligomers interact with synapses? This is currently under investigation and it is not yet known if the oligomers have specific effects at the different receptors involved in synaptic plasticity, or if they have a more general effect on the synaptic membranes (Shankar and Walsh, 2009). One type of receptor involved in memory formation is the NMDA receptor (named after a substance that acts as an agonist at this receptor, *N*-methyl-D-aspartic acid). NMDA receptors are activated by glutamate, the main excitatory neurotransmitter in the brain. A number of studies have shown that amyloid oligomers disrupt this neurotransmitter system, possibly by increasing levels of glutamate. Excess glutamate is harmful to neurons and causes damage by a process known as excitotoxicity. Research in this area has led to the development of drugs targeting the NMDA receptor, which will be described in the next chapter.

Exactly how this links to the loss of cholinergic neurons in AD discussed earlier is unclear. What is clear, however, is that disruptions to the glutamate neurotransmitter system, and therefore to synapse function, forms a possible route by which amyloid causes the cognitive problems seen in AD. This would happen before the more widespread damage and neuron loss associated with plaque deposition seen in the later stages of the condition. Indeed, it is now known that not only cholinergic neurons are lost in AD; **glutamatergic neurons** (neurons that release glutamate) are also lost, as are, to a lesser extent, neurons containing other neurotransmitters such as noradrenalin, serotonin and dopamine.

The discussion now turns to another characteristic feature of AD: the presence of neurofibrillary tangles in the brain.

2.6 Neurofibrillary tangles and tau

2.6.1 Microtubules and tau

This chapter has so far discussed two of the defining features of Alzheimer's dementia: the loss of neurons in specific brain regions and the presence of high levels of β-amyloid. The third characteristic pathological change seen in AD is the presence of neurofibrillary tangles (NFTs) inside neurons. As shown in Figure 2.1, these are seen as dense deposits inside neurons. Examination of these deposits reveals that they consist of threads, or fibrils (not to be confused with the amyloid fibrils), which become clumped together in bundles. The tangled appearance of the bundles of fibrils accounts for the name given to these deposits. In some instances, it can be seen that the neuron has died and the tangles occupy the space where the neuron had been. Closer analysis of the NFTs shows that they are composed of aggregates of the protein known as tau.

As is the case with β-amyloid, tau protein is a normal constituent of neurons and plays a role in their normal functioning. It is thought to be necessary for the formation and stabilisation of **microtubules** in neuronal axons (Lee et al., 2005). Microtubules fulfil two functions in neurons: they provide structure to the neuron and they transport substances along the axon as required. Figure 2.15a shows a segment of a microtubule with tau protein attached and its position inside the axon of a neuron.

■ Can you think of any substances that may need to be transported along axons to the axon terminal?

☐ There are many, but you may have thought of neurotransmitters or enzymes that are involved in the formation or breakdown of neurotransmitters.

The presence of NFTs is not unique to AD; in fact, they are found in a group of so-called 'tauopathies', which include some other dementias and neurological disorders (for example some cases of frontotemporal dementia, as described in Chapter 1). They are, however, found in high levels in the brain areas associated with neuron loss in AD, such as the hippocampus and parts of the cortex (Rubio et al., 2006). It therefore seems important to investigate the role of NFTs in the pathology of AD and the links between NFTs, amyloid plaques and loss of neurons. The same questions arise as before (Section 2.5.2) regarding the order of appearance of the pathologies, any possible causal links between them, and any relevance of the pathology to the development of symptoms.

The next section explains what goes wrong in the normal process of tau biology and how this affects the neuron.

2.6.2 Formation of tangles

Tau protein binds to microtubules and helps them to assemble into structures that run the length of the axon. The extent of the binding depends on a particular property of the tau protein, and that is the number of phosphate groups that the protein contains.

It has been found that tau protein with few phosphate groups attached binds with high affinity to microtubules. By contrast, tau with many phosphate groups attached is less effective at binding to microtubules (Figure 2.15b). In NFTs, the tau protein contains an abnormally high number of phosphate groups and as such it is said to be a **hyperphosphorylated** form of tau.

A phosphate group is a part of a molecule containing phosphorus and oxygen. Many proteins change their properties by the addition or removal of phosphate groups.

■ What effect would the presence of high levels of hyperphosphorylated tau have on neuronal function?

☐ It would prevent effective assembly of microtubules and therefore affect the structural integrity of the neuron and reduce the efficiency of transport of substances along the axon.

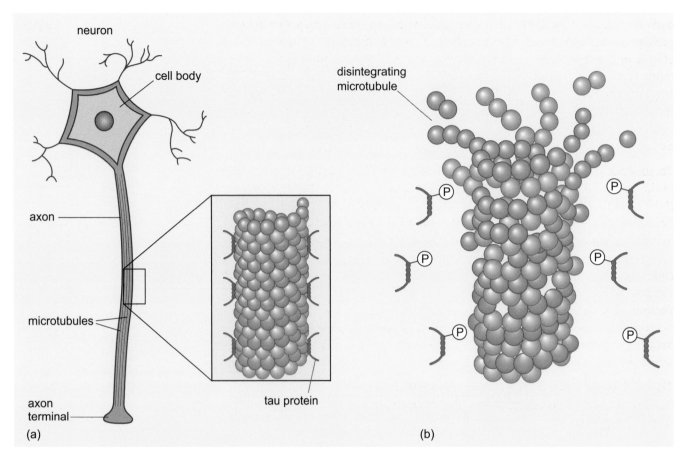

Figure 2.15 (a) Diagram of a neuron showing microtubules inside the axon. The enlarged section shows tau binding to, and enabling the formation of, the microtubule. (b) Diagram showing disintegration of the microtubule when tau is hyperphosphorylated (as denoted by P) and therefore not bound to the microtubule.

The logical conclusion, therefore, would be that the abnormal form of tau prevents effective functioning of the neuron, which would eventually die, leaving behind a tangle of the aggregated protein. Some studies support the notion that NFTs are the cause of neuron death, but others suggest that this is not the case. One alternative suggestion is that the formation of NFTs may actually protect the neuron against further damage (Lee et al., 2005).

2.6.3 Plaques, tangles and neuron loss

How does the formation of NFTs fit into the amyloid cascade hypothesis as discussed in Section 2.5? Remember that current theories suggest that soluble oligomers of β-amyloid are the initial cause of neuronal dysfunction and that plaque formation occurs after the initial damage has been done. It is possible that the formation of NFTs is also a form of secondary damage rather than being involved in the onset of AD. In support of this, many studies using neuronal cell cultures have shown that β-amyloid increases the production of hyperphosphorylated tau in neurons, leading to an accumulation of tau protein and loss of binding to microtubules (Rubio et al., 2006). These studies would seem to support the theory that attack by β-amyloid is the initial event in neuron toxicity, but also that the formation of NFTs is an integral part of the pathological process. Rather than a sequence of events, the hypothesis can perhaps be seen as a web of interacting factors. It has been suggested that the effects of β-amyloid on synapse function are subtle to begin with, but become more severe as the condition progresses. In parallel with these changes, amyloid and tau deposits are built up, which add to the damage. Eventually there is disruption of many neuronal cell processes, leading to widespread neuronal dysfunction and ultimately death of neurons (Haass and Selkoe, 2007).

To summarise Sections 2.5 and 2.6, there are two characteristic deposits seen in the brains of people with AD: amyloid plaques and neurofibrillary tangles (NFTs). Amyloid plaques are formed as the end point of a process involving excessive production of the peptide β-amyloid. The amyloid cascade hypothesis proposes that β-amyloid is central to the development of AD symptoms and recent evidence suggests that small aggregates of β-amyloid, called oligomers, are responsible for the initial damage to neurons by affecting synapse function. NFTs are produced due to the effects of an abnormal version of the protein tau. Deposits of amyloid and tau contribute to the neurodegeneration seen in AD. The three main pathological features of AD – neuron loss, amyloid plaques and NFTs – are therefore linked in a complex series of events.

The next section describes new developments in the identification of biological changes in AD and how this research may lead to more accurate diagnostic procedures.

2.7   Biomarkers for Alzheimer's dementia

A **biomarker** is a specific biological change associated with a disorder that can be used for diagnosis. A biomarker can be a structural change in the body or a particular molecule that can be detected in one of the tissues of the body. Ideally it should be possible to detect a biomarker early on in the disorder, before symptoms are so severe that any treatment will be ineffective. This is particularly important in Alzheimer's dementia, where existing therapies are most beneficial at the early stages of the condition. Biomarkers should also be specific for a particular disorder, in order to discriminate between patients with similar signs and symptoms.

Biomarkers can be used to measure the progression of a disorder and to monitor the response of individuals to particular treatments. They can also be used as measures in clinical trials for assessing the benefits of new treatments. There has been a huge research effort in recent years to identify potential biomarkers for AD, in the hope that accurate diagnosis in the early stages of the condition will become possible.

■   Can you think of any possible biomarkers for AD?

□   You may have thought of: a structural change in the brain, for example the size of the hippocampus; a molecule related to the amyloidogenic pathway, such as β-amyloid; or abnormal tau.

Section 2.2.1 described some of the uses of brain scanning techniques in research and diagnosis of AD. As techniques improve and scanning equipment becomes more readily available, several measures are being evaluated for their usefulness in improving diagnosis. These include hippocampal volume, cortical volume, whole brain volume, cortical thickness, hippocampal blood flow and amyloid plaque deposition. A note of caution is that there is considerable variation in these factors within the human population and as a consequence these techniques are unlikely to be useful as sole biomarkers for AD. Nevertheless, the techniques are good at monitoring change and therefore the progression of the condition. They may also be useful to supplement other tests used in diagnosis.

Moving on to biological molecules, the most obvious candidates for biomarkers in AD are the 42 amino acid form of β-amyloid and hyperphosphorylated tau. Both of these substances can be detected in the CSF (cerebrospinal fluid, Book 2, Section 2.2.6) and the test is reported to be between 80% and 90% reliable in detecting AD (Schneider et al., 2009). Research is currently being carried out to establish the significance of these CSF biomarkers and their relationship to structural brain changes and dementia ratings. They are being used in some clinical trials to monitor the effects of new drug treatments on amyloid and tau levels. However, CSF testing is unlikely to become widely used in early diagnosis, as the collection of spinal fluid is a complex procedure with some associated risk.

Less invasive procedures using **blood plasma** or **blood serum** for the detection of biomarkers have been explored. (Blood plasma is prepared from blood by removing the blood cells and platelets; blood serum is prepared by removing cells, platelets and other factors.) Several different categories of biomarker for AD that can be detected in blood samples have been reported and these are summarised in Table 2.1. In most of the categories there are several different molecules that can be measured, thus providing an array of measurements, referred to in some media reports as an 'Alzheimer's barcode'. It should be stressed that at the time of writing (2010) these biomarkers are being evaluated and there are no diagnostic tests currently available based on blood samples.

The future for the diagnosis of AD in its early stages, based on the above findings, is very hopeful. It is likely that in the near future a definitive diagnosis of AD will be possible, based on behavioural and cognitive evaluation reinforced with one or more of the biomarker tests described here. Preliminary findings reported by the UK Alzheimer's Society (2010) suggest that the combination of a brain scan and a blood test for a new protein biomarker is 90% accurate in predicting the onset of AD in patients with mild memory impairment.

Table 2.1 Categories of biomarkers derived from blood samples with potential for the diagnosis of Alzheimer's dementia. Adapted from Schneider et al. (2009).

Biomarker	Comment
Markers related to the amyloidogenic pathway	See Section 2.5
Markers of tau	See Section 2.6
Markers related to cholesterol metabolism	High cholesterol may be associated with a higher risk of developing AD; this will be discussed in the next section and in Chapter 3.
Markers of oxidation	It is thought that oxidative stress, or the damage to neurons by too much oxygen, plays a role in the development of AD pathology
Markers of immunological mechanisms and inflammation	The importance of inflammation in the development of AD is discussed in Chapter 3
Markers of microvascular (small blood vessel) changes	The role of vascular factors in AD is discussed in Chapter 3
Genetic markers	Particular genes associated with an increased risk of AD are discussed in Section 2.9

The next two sections of this chapter describe the difficulties in establishing an initial cause for AD and discuss the identification of risk factors associated with the condition. We start with a discussion of possible environmental factors and health problems that may be linked to an increased likelihood of developing AD.

2.8 Risk factors for Alzheimer's dementia

As discussed in Section 1.2.3, the main risk factor for Alzheimer's dementia is age. But this doesn't mean that the development of AD, or any other form of dementia, is inevitable in old age. Despite all the knowledge that we now have about the biological changes in AD, we still don't know very much about why some individuals develop the condition and some do not. The initial cause or stimulus for the onset of AD remains unidentified, if indeed there is one single cause. It is likely that different events cause the onset of AD in different people. Much research has focused on environmental or health risk factors that increase the likelihood of a person developing the dementia. Most of the evidence for possible risk factors is based on epidemiological research, which mainly makes use of correlational studies (Book 1, Section 4.2.5).

■ Can you recall the distinction between correlational studies and experimental studies?

□ Correlational studies involve observations of the relationships between one variable and another, while experimental studies involve manipulation of the variables by the experimenter in order to measure the effect of one variable on another (Book 1, Box 4.5).

■ What might an epidemiological study of an environmental risk factor for AD involve?

☐ It might involve recording the prevalence of AD in populations of people exposed to a particular environmental factor, compared with populations not exposed to that factor. Or it could involve recording the incidence of AD at different levels of exposure to the environmental factor.

From the last answer, you may be able to see the problems associated with this sort of study. Environmental influences encompass everything that an individual is exposed to, including the physical environment, social factors, diet, lifestyle, education, and so on. It is impossible to separate out one factor from another in an individual's life history and environmental influences do not remain constant throughout an individual's life. Furthermore, influences may be additive or one influence may counteract another, so clearly there are a number of ways that the development of AD could be influenced. It is also possible that environmental factors do not influence AD directly, but increase the likelihood of developing another health problem which in turn contributes to the development of AD. As for the investigation of health risk factors, it is likely that people have more than one condition at the same time: for example, obesity and heart disease.

Nevertheless, several factors have been investigated as possible risk factors for AD and these are known as **candidate risk factors**. The term 'candidate' means that the factor is not definitely involved, but there is usually some evidence suggesting an involvement. Some candidate risk factors for AD are listed in Table 2.2. You may be able to add to the list if you have read any news stories about factors contributing to AD.

Table 2.2 Candidate risk factors for Alzheimer's dementia. Compiled from the UK Alzheimer's Society (2010), Jedrziewski et al. (2005) and Mucke (2009).

Dietary factors (e.g. high cholesterol, low levels of particular vitamins)
Poor social engagement
Poor physical activity
Low level of mental stimulation
Low level of education
Excess alcohol intake
Smoking
Exposure to metals (e.g. aluminium)
Head trauma
Oestrogen decline
Obesity
Diabetes
Hypertension (high blood pressure)
Cardiovascular disease

There is not the space to discuss the evidence for all of the risk factors mentioned in this section, but we will briefly look at two factors: aluminium and lack of physical activity.

Aluminium was first suggested as a risk factor for AD in the mid-1960s. At its simplest, the idea was that an excess of aluminium in water and diet leads to AD. The main evidence linking aluminium to AD is that the metal is found in amyloid plaques and NFTs in the brains of people with AD.

■ Does this finding prove that aluminium is responsible for the development of AD?

☐ No, it does not prove this. The presence of aluminium in plaques and tangles is a correlation and does not prove that aluminium causes the abnormalities.

Other experimental studies in animals and neuronal cell cultures have shown that aluminium is toxic to neurons, but the concentrations of aluminium used were much higher than those experienced by humans. Epidemiological studies are difficult because aluminium is so widespread in the environment, and so far studies have failed to show a link between sources of aluminium and AD. The UK Alzheimer's Society (2010) holds the view that there is no convincing demonstration of a causal relationship between aluminium and AD.

The evidence for the involvement of physical activity levels is a little more convincing, although there is still inconsistency between the findings of different studies (reviewed in Jedrziewski et al., 2005). Many of the studies have focused on the effects of exercise on cognitive performance, and a meta-analysis (Book 2, Box 1.7) of 18 longitudinal studies shows that greater physical activity is associated with greater cognitive improvement. One study reports that more frequent and intense exercise is related to a lower risk of developing AD and other dementias (excluding vascular dementia). There have been attempts to investigate this link using animal models: for example, one study using transgenic mice showed that mice provided with running wheels had lower levels of β-amyloid deposits in the brain compared with control mice, which were not provided with running wheels. The mice with running wheels also showed an increase in the speed at which they learned new tasks.

So, does knowledge of particular risk factors for AD lead to the possibility of preventing the condition from developing? Is it possible to delay or prevent symptoms by engaging in stimulating activities? We will return to this topic in Chapter 4.

The next section turns to a discussion of the genetics of AD and particular genes that are associated with an increased risk of developing the disorder.

2.9 Genetics of Alzheimer's dementia

2.9.1 Early onset Alzheimer's dementia

Early onset Alzheimer's dementia is defined as the appearance of AD symptoms before the age of 65. It is much less common than **late onset Alzheimer's dementia** and it can have a genetic basis (referred to as familial early onset Alzheimer's dementia). The development of dementia in relatively early life is clearly extremely distressing to the person affected and to their family and friends, as is the case with late onset AD.

Family studies have shown that some forms of early onset AD show a high level of heritability from one generation to the next. A huge research effort has taken place to identify the genes involved in this heritability. The first gene to be investigated was the gene that produces the protein APP. As this gene is present in everyone, the researchers were looking for slight changes in the gene, or mutations, which would produce a slightly altered version of the APP protein. Several different mutations of the *APP* gene have now been identified in different families with early onset AD that have various effects on the APP protein (Brouwers et al., 2008). Transgenic mice have been used to investigate the precise effects of the abnormal *APP* genes and how they lead to AD pathology.

APP mutations only account for a small percentage of cases of familial early onset AD and to date two other genes have been implicated, known as presenilin 1 and 2 (*PSEN1* and *PSEN2*), which also have many different mutations. The presenilin proteins are thought to be involved in the processing of APP.

The effects of these mutated genes include increased production of the longer 42 amino acid form of β-amyloid and consequently increased aggregation of β-amyloid, thus showing a clear link between abnormal genes and the pathology of AD.

Although familial early onset AD is very rare, the study of the gene mutations mentioned above has advanced our understanding of the biological processes involved in AD enormously.

2.9.2 Exploring the genetics of late onset Alzheimer's dementia

The genetic basis for late onset AD is not nearly as clear-cut as for familial early onset AD as described in the last section. There does appear to be a significant genetic component of the late onset form of the dementia, but the inheritance pattern is more variable and the genes identified for familial early onset AD do not seem to be involved. It is thought that many different genes have a role in increasing the likelihood of developing late onset AD. Genes that increase the risk of developing a disorder are sometimes referred to as **susceptibility genes** to distinguish them from genes with a more direct causal link to the disorder.

One gene in particular has been identified as a potential risk factor for late onset AD and studied extensively. This gene produces the protein apolipoprotein E (ApoE), which in normal circumstances is involved in cholesterol transport round the body but is also found in association with β-amyloid in AD brains. There are three variants (or alleles, see Book 2, Section 2.4.1) of the gene, producing proteins known as ApoE-E2, ApoE-E3 and ApoE-E4. The gene producing the E3 version of the protein is the most common in the population. It has been found that people with the E4 variant have a higher risk of developing AD compared to the rest of the population, while people with the E2 variant have a lower risk. Cell culture studies indicate that ApoE-E4 binds to β-amyloid and increases its formation into deposits (Brouwers et al., 2008). Also, studies in mice show that ApoE-E4 increases amyloid plaque formation compared to ApoE-E3.

Many studies have attempted to establish the exact increase in risk of developing AD associated with the *ApoE-E4* allele, but it is difficult to state an exact figure as several different methods have been used. There is a general agreement that the known genetic risk factors do not account for all of the heritability of AD and that other genes or environmental factors must be involved (Ertekin-Taner, 2007). At the time of writing (2010), there are reports of several other susceptibility genes associated with an increased risk of developing AD.

Activity 2.5 Benefits of genetic research
(LO 2.2) Allow 10 minutes

Make a list of the potential benefits of genetic research in AD.

Some of the outcomes of genetic research, such as the development of genetic testing, could be seen as controversial. For example, there are ethical issues associated with performing genetic tests for a disorder with no effective treatments. Also, the results of genetic testing can easily be misinterpreted. As you have seen above, for most cases of AD the presence of a gene associated with the dementia implies an increased risk of developing AD but that risk may still be very small. The development of AD depends on a range of other factors, not yet completely determined, in addition to particular genes. There are concerns that people who have had positive test results for particular genes could be discriminated against, for example by insurance companies or employers. In fact, such discrimination is probably rare, but increasing awareness is forcing governments to introduce legislation to protect individuals. For example, in 2008 the Genetic Information Nondiscrimination Act was signed in the USA to protect against discrimination in health insurance and employment settings.

2.10 Final word

You have seen in this chapter that there is a wealth of knowledge about the biological changes that occur in Alzheimer's dementia. A picture is being built up of the various factors involved in neurodegeneration and how these factors interact. The development of AD is unlikely to be a simple stepwise sequence of events, but rather a complex set of interactions with many events leading to neuronal damage. You have also seen that genetics plays a part, but in most cases of AD there are other factors involved in the initiation of the condition. The initial stimulus or cause of the dementia remains unclear, but it is likely that genetic and environmental factors combine to increase the likelihood of developing AD. The research that has been carried out into the biological bases of AD has allowed the development of new methods of diagnosis and treatment. This chapter has focused on the biology of AD and in the next chapter you will read about various treatment strategies that target the changes in brain biology in this devastating mental health condition.

2.11 Summary of Chapter 2

- Alzheimer's dementia is associated with three characteristic pathological changes in the brain: decreased volume due to death of neurons; β-amyloid deposits (amyloid plaques); and neurofibrillary tangles (NFTs).

- The structural and functional changes in AD can be studied using brain scanning techniques such as MRI, fMRI and PET.

- Animal models and cell culture techniques have been used extensively to investigate the biological changes in AD.

- The cholinergic hypothesis states that the decline of cognitive function seen in AD is due to a loss of cholinergic neurons in the brain.

- The amyloid cascade hypothesis suggests a central role for β-amyloid in the development of AD.

- Recent evidence suggests that amyloid oligomers disrupt the function of synapses by interacting with the glutamate neurotransmitter system, leading to neuron dysfunction and ultimately death of neurons.

- Amyloid plaques and NFTs add to the neuronal damage at later stages of the cascade.

- A number of environmental, health and genetic factors are thought to be associated with an increased risk of developing AD.

2.12 Learning outcomes

LO 2.1 Explain current theories of the biological basis for the development of Alzheimer's dementia and how changes in brain biology may lead to the symptoms of AD. (KU2)

LO 2.2 Describe current knowledge about the genetic basis for AD. (KU2)

LO 2.3 Describe the methods used to obtain evidence for the biological basis of AD, including the use of animal models. (KU5, CS1, CS2)

LO 2.4 Analyse and interpret evidence from experiments shown in graphs or tables and interpret theoretical information about the biological basis of AD shown in diagrammatic form. (CS3, KS1, PS1)

LO 2.5 Describe the limits of current knowledge and some of the difficulties associated with research into the causes of AD. (CS4)

2.13 Self-assessment questions

SAQ 2.1 (LO 2.3)

A researcher wants to investigate the activity in a particular area of the cortex during a learning task in a person with AD. What method should be used for this study?

SAQ 2.2 (LO 2.5)

Why has it been so difficult to investigate correlations between the extent of AD pathology and the severity of symptoms in humans?

SAQ 2.3 (LO 2.1)

What are the main components of amyloid plaques and neurofibrillary tangles, respectively? How does each substance differ from the usual version of the substance found in neurons?

SAQ 2.4 (LO 2.2)

Why do you think most transgenic animal models of AD use human genes associated with familial early onset AD rather than late onset AD?

Chapter 3 Pharmacological approaches to the treatment of Alzheimer's dementia

Katherine Leys, Claire Rostron and Christine Heading

3.1 Introduction

This chapter continues the focus of the previous chapter on Alzheimer's dementia and will examine the drug treatments or **pharmacotherapies** that currently exist for the cognitive symptoms of AD, such as memory impairment, and those that exist for the non-cognitive or behavioural symptoms. We will evaluate the evidence for the **efficacy** of these available treatments (their ability to produce the desired clinical effect) and look at the problems of using drugs to treat this complex condition. The chapter will also examine the research that is currently taking place for the development of new pharmacotherapies for AD and the advances that are being made. We will look at new ideas for treatments based on the evidence that AD is an inflammatory disorder or linked to vascular disease. By the end of the chapter, you should have an understanding of the usefulness and limitations of current drug treatments and whether there is any hope for a curative drug treatment in the near future.

3.2 Treating the cognitive symptoms of Alzheimer's dementia

This section will explore the drug treatments that are currently available for the cognitive symptoms of AD such as those measured using the MMSE rating system (Section 1.4.2). We will look at the older, typical drug treatments that target the **cholinergic** system before moving on to the newer drug memantine which acts on pathways involving the neurotransmitter glutamate. But first we will start with a brief discussion of some of the challenges of designing effective and acceptable drug treatments for AD.

3.2.1 Pharmacological treatment challenges

When designing a pharmacological treatment for any mental ill-health condition, as indeed with any physical ill-health condition, one of the main considerations is how to get enough of the drug to the required physiological region. When administering a drug, the amount that enters the bloodstream is called the **bioavailability** of the drug. Different drug treatments have very different degrees of bioavailability and this is important for working out the dose that is needed. The bioavailability of drugs administered in tablet form varies widely, depending on how much of the drug is absorbed by the stomach or intestines. Drugs administered by injection have high bioavailability, as the drug enters the bloodstream directly. In addition, if the brain is the desired site of action, the drug must be able to cross the blood–brain barrier (Book 2, Box 3.5).

Another factor to consider is the length of time that a drug stays in the body at effective doses. The duration of a drug's effects depends on how quickly the body can remove it from the blood system once it has been absorbed. This is sometimes referred to as the **plasma half-life**, which is the length of time it takes for the body to reduce the concentration of the drug by half. Drugs with a long plasma half-life are removed from the body at a slow rate; therefore the effects of the drug will remain for longer than for drugs with a short plasma half-life.

Bioavailability and duration of action of a drug depend on many factors, including the properties of the drug and the method of administration. In the treatment of AD, drugs are normally administered orally in tablet form, as this is a method that can be managed most easily and results in greater **compliance** with the medication. Compliance refers to the extent to which a person actually takes the dose prescribed and is a significant problem for people with AD, because of their memory and behavioural problems. A simple administration method, high bioavailability so that low doses are required, and a long plasma half-life so that doses are required as few times daily as possible, would be the most desirable form of treatment for AD.

Another potential problem for any drug treatment is the possibility of side effects, or unwanted effects caused by the drug having actions other than the required action. This is a particular problem for AD treatments that target the cholinergic system, because the neurotransmitter acetylcholine has a very widespread distribution throughout the body (Figure 3.1). This distribution includes the **gastrointestinal system**, which includes the oesophagus, stomach and small and large intestines. Therefore, all of the available cholinergic treatments for AD have the potential to cause severe side effects such as anorexia, nausea, vomiting and diarrhoea. If patients find these side effects intolerable, compliance may be affected.

3.2.2 Treating the loss of brain acetylcholine

Chapter 2 argued that one well-known and scientifically accepted brain change in a person with Alzheimer's dementia is the loss of neurons that use acetylcholine as a neurotransmitter. The loss of these neurons is significant because they have been shown to be important for learning, memory and attention. Several experimental lines of evidence to support this contention were discussed including evidence from animal studies.

Most of the available drug treatments that may be prescribed for someone with AD focus on increasing levels of acetylcholine in the brain to compensate for the reduction in the natural levels of this neurotransmitter.

■   Can you think of any ways that one might theoretically increase the level of cholinergic activity in the brain?

☐   You might have thought of increasing acetylcholine synthesis or increasing its release from the presynaptic neuron. Levels of acetylcholine could be increased at the synapse by inhibiting its breakdown. Alternatively, cholinergic activity could be increased by using an agonist at the cholinergic receptor.

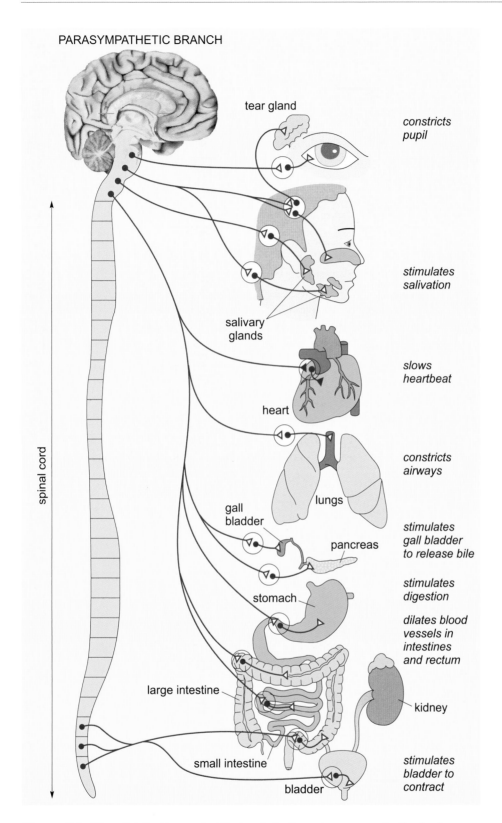

Figure 3.1 The distribution and effects of cholinergic neurons in the body. Neurons with axon terminals represented as unfilled triangles have an excitatory effect, neurons with axon terminals represented as filled triangles have an inhibitory effect.

These approaches are summarised in Table 3.1.

Table 3.1 Ways in which drugs could theoretically increase the levels of cholinergic activity within the brain.

Drug serves as a precursor for acetylcholine, increasing the levels of one of the chemical substances from which acetylcholine is made

Drug activates the synthesis enzyme choline acetyltransferase (ChAT), increasing the amount of acetylcholine that can be produced

Drug increases the storage of acetylcholine within the presynaptic neuron, making it readily available for release at the synapse

Drug stimulates the release of acetylcholine at the synapse

Drug acts as an agonist of acetylcholine by stimulating its receptors

Drug blocks the breakdown of acetylcholine by the enzyme acetylcholinesterase

Despite the wide variety of possibilities, all drugs that target acetylcholine for the treatment of AD act on the enzyme that breaks it down. This enzyme is called **acetylcholinesterase** (or **AChE**). AChE should not be confused with the enzyme ChAT, which you encountered in Section 2.3.2. ChAT is used to make acetylcholine, while the enzyme AChE is used to break it down. The drugs that act on AChE are known as **anticholinesterases** because they block its action. These anticholinesterases include donepezil, rivastigmine and galantamine, drugs that are commercially known as Aricept®, Exelon® and Reminyl®, respectively. The actions of the anticholinesterases that are important for the treatment of AD occur at cholinergic synapses in the cortex and hippocampus. However, as discussed above, targeting any drug treatment to a very specific region of the brain and/or body is extremely difficult.

3.2.3 Prescribing cholinergic drug treatments in practice

The possible side effects of drugs that act on the cholinergic system have been mentioned above. A prescribing physician, such as a UK General Practitioner, bases the choice of prescription drug on the ability of the patient to cope with the various side effects that occur, weighed against the maximal dose needed for benefit. This process occurs through consultation with the carers of the person with AD. Usually patients start with a low dose, which is increased in stages to the highest dose that can be tolerated. In this way, tolerance to the side effects is usually improved.

Each of the drugs previously mentioned has very different characteristics. For example, donepezil has high bioavailability and a long plasma half-life, so only needs to be administered once a day. As a result, donepezil is usually the drug of choice for the treatment of AD. Galantamine has high bioavailability but a short half-life, although a slow-release formulation is available which is only required once a day. Rivastigmine has low bioavailability and a very short half-life, so twice daily doses are needed. Side effects appear to be more common with this drug. RCTs (randomised controlled trials; Book 2, Box 3.3) have shown that at the doses of rivastigmine necessary for maximum effect, there is a tendency for large numbers of people to withdraw from the studies due to the severity of the side effects experienced (Davis, 2008). So, while the effects of rivastigmine may appear to be good in terms of actual improvements in cognition and overall function, practically speaking it seems many individuals cannot tolerate the dose needed to achieve this effect. For this reason, a skin patch form of rivastigmine (this method of administration is referred to as a **transdermal route of administration**) has recently been developed, which provides a more constant level of the drug in the body and avoids the fluctuations in levels experienced when the drug is administered orally. This has been evaluated and found to lead to fewer adverse gastrointestinal effects compared to the tablet form of rivastigmine (Sadowsky et al., 2010).

Activity 3.1 The action of anticholinesterases
(LO 3.1) Allow 20 minutes

Now would be a good time to view the animation of the effects of application of the anticholinesterases within the AD brain in the multimedia map. You should ensure that you are familiar with the mechanism of action of these drugs before leaving the activity and returning to the chapter. You might wish to take notes and to draw diagrams to help you remember this process.

Mark (Book 1, Section 1.1.1) is in the moderate stage of AD and so he has been prescribed donepezil (Aricept®). A clinical psychologist will assess Mark as being within the moderate stage if his MMSE score falls within the range of 10 to 20. Until recently (late 2010), NICE (National Institute for Health and Clinical Excellence) guidelines have not recommended the use of the available anticholinesterase drug treatments in the early stages of AD. There has been resistance to this guideline for two reasons. The first is that it seems counterintuitive not to prescribe a drug treatment as early as possible in the course of an illness, if an effective drug treatment exists. This is particularly important in AD, as you will see later. The second is that the MMSE represents a restricted view of symptoms and therefore the potential to respond to this drug. However, the NICE guidelines are recommendations only and in practice many UK practitioners have prescribed donepezil in the early stage of AD. There is unfortunately a degree of regional variation in this practice (Dening, 2009). (At the time of writing (October 2010), NICE has published draft guidelines recommending that anticholinesterases should be available to people in the early to moderate stages of AD. Final decisions on this are expected by the end of 2010.)

Returning to Mark, his prognosis is rather gloomy. His donepezil will only postpone the worsening of his symptoms for between six and 12 months, and he may well be within the 50% of cases for which there is no response to any form of cholinergic drug therapy. However, if he can tolerate the side effects, and he is responsive, there is some evidence to suggest that his cognitive function will remain stable, or decline more slowly than it would have done without this drug. It is to this evidence that we will now turn.

3.2.4 Evaluating the efficacy of cholinergic drug treatments

Anticholinesterases have been collectively evaluated by the process of meta-analysis (Book 2, Box 1.7) for the treatment of early to moderate stage dementia. They were found to have consistent positive effects on cognition (Ralna et al., 2008). However, this study concluded that the size of the positive effects is very small and that many studies show only short-term effects, in the order of six months. Similarly, in a paper for the American College of Physicians, only weak recommendations could be made regarding the prescription of anticholinesterases because the effects of these drugs were considered too small. An urgent need for more research was also noted in this paper (Qaseem et al., 2008).

It is possible that you will be familiar with the debate on prescribing policy for dementia drugs from media coverage. Given the particular controversy surrounding the NICE decision in 2007 to recommend anticholinesterases only in the moderate stage of AD, what is the evidence that they might be effective in the early stage specifically? One RCT by Ben Seltzer and colleagues (Seltzer et al., 2004) evaluated treatment by donepezil for early AD using change in the MMSE score as their measure of efficacy. The results of this study are shown in Figure 3.2.

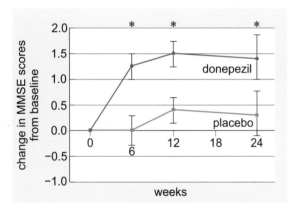

Figure 3.2 Mean change (± SEM) in MMSE scores in early AD after treatment with donepezil or a placebo. The results are shown as the change from baseline scores recorded at the start of the study, over 24 weeks of treatment. The asterisks denote a significant difference between the results obtained in the two groups.

■ Does treatment with donepezil have benefits over treatment with placebo in this study?

□ Yes. The results at six weeks, 12 weeks and 24 weeks all show an improvement from baseline of around 1.0 to 1.5 points on the MMSE.

These results suggest that donepezil has only a very small improvement effect in the early stage of AD, in line with the results of the meta-analysis for the early to moderate stages of the condition. However, these results, and the debate that rages on internationally, raise the question of what constitutes a worthwhile benefit of a health care intervention for AD. How much of an improvement is worth the cost of delivering the intervention? Clearly, for policymakers at least, a small improvement like that shown in the anticholinesterase studies is not enough, but patients and carers may hold a different view. The potential to utilise this view to improve care for people with dementia is discussed later, in Chapter 4.

3.2.5 Nicotine and Alzheimer's dementia

The anticholinesterases described in the previous sections are established pharmacotherapies for AD and there is consistent evidence that they have a small effect on cognitive performance, at least in the early to middle stages of the condition. What about other ways of targeting the cholinergic neurotransmitter system? Remember from Table 3.1 that there are many theoretical ways of replacing the cholinergic activity that is lost in AD. There have been various reports over the last few years that nicotine, in the form of smoking, may have beneficial effects for people with AD or may even be a protective factor against AD. The idea has its basis in the fact that nicotine is a cholinergic agonist at one type of cholinergic receptor, called the nicotinic acetylcholine receptor (Book 3, Section 2.3.2), which has reduced levels in the AD brain. In theory, then, the use of nicotine could compensate for the loss of cholinergic activity in AD by acting on the remaining nicotinic receptors. If cholinergic activity is reduced in the initial stages of the dementia, smoking could perhaps delay the onset of symptoms. Epidemiological studies of the risk of developing AD in smokers and non-smokers have, however, produced mixed results, so no consistent evidence has emerged that smoking protects against AD. In fact, you may recall from the previous chapter (Table 2.2) that smoking is one of the candidate factors for increasing the risk of developing AD. Results from animal models have also been contradictory. For example, some studies in mice indicate that nicotine reduces levels of amyloid plaque formation (Rubio et al., 2006), yet other studies suggest that nicotine has no effect on levels of soluble amyloid and it actually enhances the levels of hyperphosphorylated tau (Oddo et al., 2005). See Box 3.1 for a recent extract from a health website citing the views of one group of researchers in this area.

Box 3.1 Smoking and Alzheimer's dementia

The final excuse for smoking – that it might reduce the risk of developing Alzheimer's dementia – has just been stubbed out, findings from an animal study suggest.

- Past animal and human studies have indicated that nicotine exposure inhibits the formation of amyloid plaque, a key feature of Alzheimer's dementia.
- However, the new study shows that chronic nicotine use appears to worsen the effects of a brain protein called tau, which is responsible for the fibrous tangles that are the other hallmark of the disease.
- So, at best, the effects of nicotine are probably cancelled out, according to the researchers.
- Dr Frank M. LaFerla, from the University of California at Irvine, and colleagues administered nicotine to a genetically engineered strain of mice that develops Alzheimer's dementia.
- Nicotine treatment produced an increase in nicotine receptors in the animals' brains that correlated with a dramatic rise in the aggregation and activity of the tau protein.
- This indicates that the disease-causing effects of tau were worsened, the team reports in the *Proceedings of the National Academy of Sciences*.
- Moreover, in these experiments, chronic nicotine administration had no effect on levels of soluble amyloid, the researchers point out.
- The results emphasise the importance of assessing nicotine's affects on all aspects of the disease, they write.
- 'Our findings suggest that the use of nicotine as a potential therapy for Alzheimer's dementia should be reevaluated.'

(HealthCentral OurAlzheimer's.com, 2008)

The discussion now turns to a drug that acts on glutamate pathways in the brain and the evidence for its efficacy in treating AD.

3.2.6 Memantine: an alternative to cholinergic drug therapy

There is an alternative to anticholinesterase drugs for the treatment of cognitive symptoms of Alzheimer's dementia. This alternative drug, called memantine (commercially it is called Ebixa®), acts on a different neurotransmitter pathway: the glutamate pathway. Glutamate is a neurotransmitter that binds to several different receptor types within the brain to cause activation of neurons that have these receptors. One of the types of receptor that glutamate binds to is the NMDA receptor (Section 2.5.4). When glutamate binds to the NMDA receptor, this causes the opening of an ion channel in the neuronal membrane. The channel is known as an ion channel because it allows substances called **ions** to flow into the neuron. Ions are chemical substances that carry an electrical charge (either positive or negative). In this case, calcium ions (which are positively charged) flow through the open ion channel and this can lead to the generation of an action potential.

Prior to the binding of glutamate, the ion channel is blocked by magnesium ions (effectively these positive ions keep the channel closed), preventing the flow of calcium ions into the neuron. To illustrate this, the ion channel is shown in Figure 3.3a in a closed (unactivated) state when magnesium sits in the channel. If glutamate is released from the presynaptic neuron and binds to the NMDA receptor in sufficient quantities, the magnesium ions are released from the ion channel and calcium ions enter the postsynaptic neuron, as shown in Figure 3.3b. It is the NMDA receptor, or more specifically, the associated ion channel, that is the target for the drug memantine.

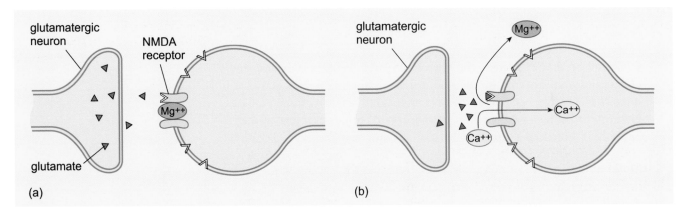

Figure 3.3 (a) A glutamatergic synapse showing the ion channel associated with the NMDA receptor in a closed state. The receptor contains a 'lock', or binding site, for the neurotransmitter glutamate. Prior to glutamate binding, the associated ion channel is blocked by magnesium ions (Mg^{++}). (b) Binding of glutamate to the receptor results in the release of magnesium ions so that calcium ions (Ca^{++}) can enter the postsynaptic neuron through the ion channel.

Research has shown that there is slightly more glutamate than normal in the brain of a person with AD. Unfortunately, too much glutamate can cause neurons to die because they become overstimulated (Section 2.5.4). It might surprise you to know that there is not, as yet, a complete understanding of how memantine works. However, this is often the case with drug discovery, where knowing how the drug works comes after the discovery that it does work! Memantine is believed to have its therapeutic effect by counteracting the effects of the mildly increased level of glutamate in AD. Therefore it is called a glutamate antagonist. Memantine acts by sitting inside the ion channel of the NMDA receptor, exactly as magnesium would do, keeping the channel from opening in response to the increased level of glutamate. However, memantine would not be a useful treatment for AD if it kept the NMDA receptor ion channel permanently closed. This is because the opening of ion channels in response to glutamate is an essential process for the formation of memories (Box 3.2). So, memantine only keeps the ion channels closed until large amounts of glutamate are released by the presynaptic neuron into the synapse. Figure 3.4a illustrates how memantine occupies the ion channel and Figure 3.4b shows how this is released when the presynaptic neuron releases further glutamate into the synapse following an action potential.

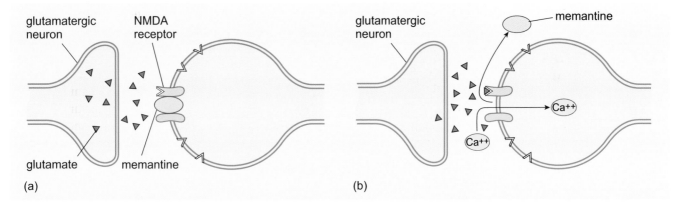

Figure 3.4 (a) The closed NMDA receptor ion channel in response to memantine. Memantine sits inside the ion channel to replace magnesium which has become lost from the channel due to the higher than normal level of glutamate in AD. (b) The open NMDA receptor ion channel, after the release of memantine following release of glutamate from the presynaptic neuron. Calcium ions can then enter the postsynaptic neuron through the ion channel.

Box 3.2 NMDA receptors and memory

The suggestion that NMDA receptors might play a crucial role in the formation of memories was first made by Richard Morris (Morris et al., 1986). He tested this idea using a task that he developed specifically to answer this question. This task is now known as the Morris water maze and you will be familiar with it from Section 2.4.2. Briefly, the task is undertaken with rats placed in a large circular pool of water and left to swim until they find an escape platform that is hidden just below the surface of the water (Figure 3.5). The measure taken in Morris's experiment was the time from first being placed in the water until the time the rat climbed onto the escape platform. This measure is known as the 'escape latency'.

Figure 3.5 A rat swimming in the Morris water maze searching for the escape platform.

In his experiment, Richard Morris administered a compound known as AP5, which is an antagonist at the NMDA receptor, directly into the hippocampus of half of the rats in the experiment, while the other half of the rats received an infusion of a control substance that had no effect on the brain. The results of this study are shown in Figure 3.6. These results show that the rats that received AP5 spent longer in the water trying to find the hidden platform compared with the control rats, even over several sessions of learning. This result was interpreted as the rats having less knowledge of where the platform was because AP5 had disrupted the formation of the platform location memory.

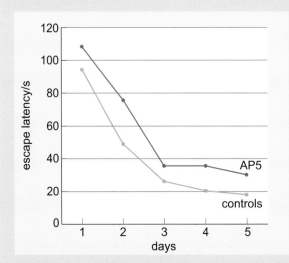

Figure 3.6 Escape latency of rats treated with the NMDA antagonist, AP5, compared with rats treated with a control substance, over 5 days of learning the task.

3.2.7 Prescribing memantine in practice

Although memantine is licensed for the treatment of moderate to severe stage AD within the UK, Mark (Section 3.2.3) is unlikely to have been prescribed memantine by his physician because until recently it has not been recommended by NICE guidelines for any stages of AD. (The October 2010 draft guidelines include a recommendation that memantine should be prescribed for late stage AD and in the moderate stage if a person cannot tolerate anticholinesterases.) Therefore in the near future, Mark could be prescribed memantine, either as a single drug therapy (referred to as **monotherapy**) or in combination with an anticholinesterase drug (referred to as **combination therapy**), potentially maximising the cognitive benefit to him. Prior to these draft guidelines, however, the UK National Health Service (NHS) believed that prescribing memantine was not a cost-effective option for people with AD. There has been a great deal of controversy surrounding this decision for the same reasons that the NICE decision about the anticholinesterases was controversial. To put this into some context, the cost of prescribing memantine is approximately £1000 per year per person, while the cost of donepezil is £1100 per year per person (depending on the dose needed). While memantine is actually slightly cheaper, the benefits of the drug are thought to be too small to make it cost-effective. What then, is the size of the effect that makes it less cost-effective than the anticholinesterases? We shall explore this issue in the next section. It is worth noting beforehand that, as with anticholinesterase drugs like rivastigmine and donepezil, memantine cannot cure AD and there is no evidence that the drug alters the underlying pathology of the illness. It only slows the progression of the symptoms. Furthermore, as with the anticholinesterases, there are some undesirable side effects of memantine. These side effects are less severe and of a different nature to those caused by anticholinesterases and can include hallucinations, dizziness, confusion, headache and tiredness. Again, these side effects occur because NMDA receptors are very widespread throughout the brain, having potentially very many functions. Unfortunately, it is impossible to target only those receptors affected in AD.

3.2.8 Evaluating the efficacy of memantine

There have been many RCTs conducted to evaluate the efficacy of memantine, but a significant problem with these RCTs is that many people taking part in them receive the drug in combination with an anticholinesterase, meaning that the specific effects of memantine are difficult to determine.

Barry Reisberg and colleagues (Reisberg et al., 2003) conducted an RCT to evaluate the efficacy of memantine in moderate to late stage AD (Figure 3.7). The study took place over 28 weeks and it was a **double blind design** (Box 3.3), meaning that neither the participants nor the experimenters knew who was receiving the drug or the placebo. The study used a measure known as the Severe Impairment Battery (SIB), which reflects cognitive performance in various domains including social interaction, memory, language, visuospatial ability and attention. It is a specially designed scale for assessing cognitive function in late stage AD when individuals cannot complete standard AD assessment tests because their impairment is so severe.

Visuospatial ability is the ability to comprehend visual representations and their spatial relationships.

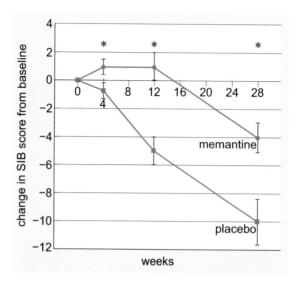

Figure 3.7 Efficacy of memantine in AD compared with placebo over 28 weeks of treatment. The graph shows the mean change (± SEM) in SIB scores for cognitive performance. The asterisks denote a significant difference between results obtained in the two groups.

■ Do the results suggest that memantine improves cognition in individuals with AD?

☐ There may be a slight improvement in SIB scores at four and 12 weeks, but overall the results show that memantine slows the rate of decline of cognition in AD, which is not the same as improving it.

These results of the study shown in Figure 3.7 reflect generally the results of RCTs to evaluate the efficacy of memantine, showing that it acts to slow cognitive decline rather than to improve performance. Although the difference in groups may initially appear quite startling, it should be noted that the performance of the memantine group at 28 weeks was similar to that of the placebo group at 12 weeks. Therefore, memantine can be concluded to have delayed the progressive decline in AD by a period of only 16 weeks.

Box 3.3 Research Methods: Blind and double blind designs

When performing an experiment or conducting an RCT, researchers must consider the possibility of a blind or double blind design. A **blind design** means that the participants are not aware of the condition they are allocated to, for example, in an RCT they would not know if they were in the drug or the placebo group. This can be arranged by having a placebo substance with the same appearance as the drug: for example, a similar-looking tablet or injection. It is more difficult to arrange when the treatment under experimentation involves a therapy such as cognitive behaviour therapy (CBT, Book 2, Section 3) or exercise. The benefit of blind trials is that participants cannot influence the outcome by having prior beliefs about the effect of particular treatments.

A double blind design means that neither the participants nor the experimenters know the group that participants have been allocated to. Again, this is easily done with drugs, but is more difficult with other types of therapies. In a double blind study, all measures should be recorded and analysed before the researchers are aware of which substance a participant has received. Double blind trials have an added benefit over blind trials in that unintentional bias on the part of the researchers cannot influence the results.

3.3 Treating the non-cognitive symptoms of Alzheimer's dementia

The drug treatments discussed so far for AD target only the cognitive decline. However, the symptoms that carers describe as being most difficult to cope with are the behavioural changes such as wandering, biting, aggressive language, and inappropriate sexual behaviour. In times gone by, it was not unusual to use severe forms of restraint as a means of dealing with these behaviours in the care setting. This has very clear ethical implications and one would hope that we could do better these days.

3.3.1 A variety of pharmacological treatments

There are many potential pharmacological treatments that are prescribed in practice for the non-cognitive symptoms of AD. These include antidepressants such as citalopram and fluoxetine, anxiolytics (drugs prescribed to reduce anxiety) such as lorazepam, and, very commonly, **antipsychotics** such as haloperidol and olanzepine. You will be familiar with the actions of some of the antidepressant and anxiolytic drugs from Book 2. For this reason we will focus on the antipsychotics here.

3.3.2 Antipsychotic drugs

Antipsychotic drugs, as the name suggests, are used in the treatment of psychotic episodes and are usually prescribed for the treatment of schizophrenia and bipolar disorder (Figure 3.8). Although we will be discussing these drugs in the context of treatment for the non-cognitive symptoms of AD, it is important to note that these drugs are not actually licensed for the treatment of AD in most countries. They are, however, frequently prescribed in Alzheimer's and other dementias to treat symptoms such as agitation.

Antipsychotics act on the mesolimbocortical dopamine pathway (this pathway is described in detail in Book 3, Section 2.1). As with all drugs, antipsychotics have their side effects, but the precise nature of these side effects depends on the particular

Figure 3.8 Antipsychotics are licensed for the treatment of psychotic episodes, not for the treatment of Alzheimer's dementia.

drug. Side effects include over-sedation, low blood pressure, dry mouth, blurred vision and weight gain. Some antipsychotics cause symptoms that are similar to those of Parkinson's disease, such as repetitive involuntary movements. As you will see below, sometimes antipsychotics have more serious side effects, which may be fatal.

Antipsychotics are antagonists at dopamine receptors, stopping the action of dopamine in its target regions (Figure 3.9). However, the loss of action of dopamine in the brain is exactly what happens naturally in Parkinson's disease when dopaminergic neurons die, and this is what causes the Parkinson's disease-like effects of some antipsychotics. Some of the newer antipsychotics, however, do not cause these symptoms.

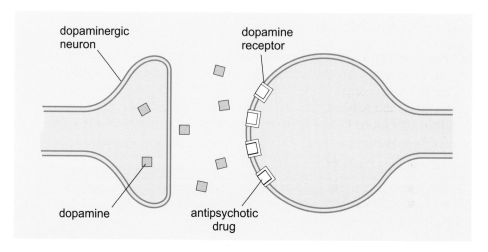

Figure 3.9 Antipsychotics act as antagonists at dopamine receptors, preventing dopamine from binding.

The use of antipsychotics to treat the non-cognitive symptoms of AD is very widespread globally. As an example, a report for the Minister of State for Care Services in the UK concluded that there were 180 000 people with dementia (of any type) within the UK taking these drugs, even though only 36 000 were likely to have a positive treatment response to them (Banerjee, 2009). The use of antipsychotics in the treatment of AD has been particularly controversial because there is an increased risk of death following their use. Studies that have investigated this risk have found a significantly increased incidence of stroke from the use of antipsychotics (Douglas and Smeeth, 2009; Gill et al., 2005). Based on the reported risk of these adverse events, Banerjee highlights that the use of antipsychotics within the UK would cause an expected 1800 deaths annually above the level typically expected as a result of age and dementia alone. Despite these very shocking statistics, the pharmacological approach remains the dominant treatment option for the non-cognitive symptoms of AD.

3.3.3 Challenging the use of antipsychotics for the treatment of dementia

In the conclusion of the report mentioned in the last section, Banerjee states that the use of antipsychotic drugs for dementia is the symptom of a cumulative failure over many years to develop effective responses to the challenges posed by AD, especially to the challenge posed by the non-cognitive symptoms. This is a very severe criticism indeed, but it is not an isolated critical opinion. In a similar vein, Box 3.4 shows the view of Clive Ballard, professor at the Institute of Psychiatry in London (Ballard and Cream, 2005).

Box 3.4 Antipsychotics and dementia: a clinican's view

As clinicians we talk about the best interests of our patients. How can a treatment which doubles the rate of cognitive decline, triples the rate of stroke, doubles mortality, substantially increases falls and fractures and reduces quality of life be beneficial […] As there is clearly no rational reason for prescribing, we need to consider other explanations.

We would suggest the following:

Therapeutic impotence: Doctors, especially specialists feel they need to do something, and prescribing a familiar drug is the easiest option.

Ignorance: Doctors are either unaware of the substantial evidence of harm with [antipsychotics] or are swayed by slick marketing information, portraying atypical[1] [antipsychotics] in an 'over-safe' light that does not reflect the actual data.

Placebo effect: If [antipsychotics] are prescribed, the majority of patients experience an improvement in BPSD[2] symptoms. This reinforces the apparent value of this practice, as we like to take the credit for any improvements that occur. The reality is that the majority of people would have experienced a comparable improvement with monitoring.

Bowing to pressure: Sometimes the pressure to respond can be great, and a prescription is an easy way to relieve the pressure. This is understandable, and reflects a similar phenomenon to that of general practitioners prescribing antibiotics for sore throats. In neither situation does it represent good practice.

Lack of skills to implement non-pharmacological alternatives: The main evidence for alternative treatment options are for therapies that by and large are not a core part of the physician or psychiatrist's skill-base, such as psychological interventions. Doctors therefore feel uncomfortable pursuing these options. Why for example is so little time spent on the non-pharmacological interventions that everyone agrees should be the first line of treatment for BPSD in people with dementia? It is largely assumed that the enlightened clinician has already appropriately assessed and diagnosed the patient and exhausted all the possible environmental and behavioural interventions before resorting to the prescription pad.

(Ballard and Cream, 2005)

[1] Atypical antipsychotics are the newer antipsychotics that are generally considered to have fewer side effects than the older, 'typical' antipsychotics.

[2] Behavioural and psychological symptoms of dementia.

Thus it needs to be asked: what are the alternative treatment options to giving someone with AD a pharmacological treatment for non-cognitive symptoms? The limitations of this biomedical approach seem very apparent. There is an alternative view of AD that brings into play both social and psychological aspects. Put simply, the alternative is to view a person with AD as someone whose personal and social capacities are changing, and that these changes are experienced as disabilities only when the environmental supports are not adapted to suit them (Gould and Kendall, 2007). **Psychosocial therapies** for the treatment of AD are based on this core idea. Generally the term 'psychosocial therapy' refers to any form of treatment that is not pharmacological. These therapies will be explored in the final chapter of this book.

Activity 3.2 Antipsychotic drugs: a carer's view
(LO 3.3) Allow 20 minutes

In the multimedia map, listen to the audio recording of Deborah talking about her mother's experience of taking antipsychotic drugs for her dementia. There are some questions for you to consider as you listen to the recording.

This chapter so far has discussed the current available drug treatments for the symptoms of Alzheimer's dementia, the extent of their efficacy and some of the problems associated with their use. The chapter will now turn to the future: what hope is there for more effective drug therapies based on current research and clinical trials? Is there any hope for a treatment that will modify or halt the progression of the dementia? The remainder of this chapter will describe some of the current research in this area.

3.4 Future directions: targeting the brain deposits of Alzheimer's dementia

3.4.1 Finding a pharmacological cure

The drug treatments described so far in this chapter are relevant to only some of the biological factors that were discussed in Chapter 2. For example, we have talked of drugs targeting the neurotransmitters acetylcholine and glutamate, but no mention has been made of targeting the characteristic plaques, tangles and neuron loss seen in AD. The reason for this is that, at the time of writing, none of the available drug treatments acts on these biological brain changes. In addition, the existing therapies target the symptoms of AD, but they are not 'disease-modifying'; in other words, they will not change the progression of the pathology. They may delay onset or progression of symptoms for a short while by altering activity at synapses, but the underlying brain changes will continue. It is thought that a cure for AD must involve preventing the pathological changes that occur in the Alzheimer's brain that lead to the death of neurons. This section examines potential therapies that target the hallmark brain deposits found in AD: amyloid and tau.

At this point, it is worth noting another problem in designing drug treatments and potential cures for AD. That is, once the illness is diagnosed, the underlying biological changes that we have explored in Chapter 2 may have progressed too far for any drug treatment to have an effect. Thus the potential success of any treatment for AD is directly linked to the problem of diagnosing early AD or identifying people at high risk of developing the condition.

3.4.2 The drug development process

Developing any new drug treatment from the research stage to obtaining a licence for human use is an extremely lengthy, costly and sometimes frustrating process. The Association of the British Pharmaceutical Industry (ABPI) estimates that the development process for a new drug takes between 10 and 12 years and costs around £500 million. This organisation also states that only one or two substances out of 10 000 tested complete the process successfully and become authorised for therapeutic use in patients. Much of the time and cost of the development process is due to the necessity to conduct clinical trials in volunteers and patients in order to assess the safety and efficacy of the potential treatment. The various stages of these clinical trials are outlined in Table 3.2. Before a substance enters clinical trials, researchers have to decide that testing in humans is worthwhile, and this decision is based on years of preclinical research using animal models, cell culture or other laboratory techniques. A patent is usually obtained for the substance at some point during the preclinical phase.

Thinking specifically of Alzheimer's dementia, it is worth noting the scale of interest. In 2009, the Pharmaceutical Research and Manufacturers of America (PhRMA) reported that there were 80 pharmacotherapies in clinical trials on behalf of US pharmaceutical and biotechnology companies (PhRMA, 2009) and there will have been hundreds, possibly thousands, of others in preclinical investigation.

Table 3.2 Phases of clinical trials for new pharmacotherapies.

Phase 1	Conducted in small numbers of healthy volunteers, or occasionally in patients unresponsive to all available treatments.
	Determines the range of doses necessary for any clinical effect and investigates tolerance, side effects and any safety issues. Assesses the pattern of absorption, distribution, breakdown and excretion of the substance.
Phase 2	Conducted in small numbers of patients with the relevant condition (up to a few hundred); usually double blind RCTs.
	Designed to test tolerance, safety and efficacy.
Phase 3	Conducted in large numbers of patients with the relevant condition (up to several thousand); usually double blind RCTs.
	Designed to further test tolerance, safety and efficacy. May test new treatment against existing standard treatments. If successful, a licence for human use is applied for.
Phase 4	Conducted after a drug has been licensed and used in large numbers of patients. Collects information about side effects, safety and long-term risks and benefits. Provides ongoing information when drug is used more widely than in RCTs.

Note: sometimes trial phases are written using the Latin numerals I, II, III and IV.

The development of new medicines takes place on a global basis but most countries maintain control over the drugs they allow to be used in their own country. Permitting a drug to be used normally involves approval by a government agency, but is quite separate from any agreement to fund its use. (Note that the National Institute for Health and Clinical Excellence (NICE) is not a regulator of medicines. Its role is to make recommendations regarding the usage of medicinal products.) Most active drugs are used in several separate products, as we can see in the UK where (in 2010) there are three anticholinesterase drugs licensed for use in AD. For each of these, several different products may be available: for example, tablets of different strengths and formulations, skin patches or injections. Drugs are usually protected by patents for a number of years, but once the patents expire, other manufacturers will probably make competitor products using the same drugs.

It is important to note that all clinical trials (and all other research studies using humans) are conducted with the consent of the participants, or their relatives if participants are unable to give their consent. Trial organisers have to ensure that participants fully understand what the trial involves and that they can withdraw from the trial at any time. This is known as **informed consent**. There are also very strict ethical standards and regulations for clinical trials which are set by regulatory bodies in individual countries. Clinical trial proposals are reviewed by ethics committees which consist of lay people, medical professionals and scientists and are independent of any interest in the outcomes of the trials.

3.4.3 Targeting the production of β-amyloid

Now that you have an understanding of the process involved in the development of a new drug treatment, this section will describe some of the research that is currently under way to find possible therapies aimed at reducing β-amyloid levels in AD. More specifically, these therapies are aimed at reducing the amount of β-amyloid produced, in the hope that the pathological process can be slowed down or even stopped completely. You may remember from Chapter 2 that the overproduction of β-amyloid, specifically the 42 amino acid version of the peptide, is thought to be a crucial part of the biology of AD. At this point, it may be worth reminding yourself of this process by revisiting the amyloid animation shown in Activity 2.4 in the multimedia map.

Production of β-amyloid is the result of initial cleavage of amyloid precursor protein (APP) by the enzyme β-secretase, followed by cleavage by another enzyme, γ-secretase. Not surprisingly, potential treatments have been investigated that reduce the production of β-amyloid by inhibiting either of these enzymes. One such substance, known as tarenflurbil, which inhibits γ-secretase, has been studied up to Phase 3 of clinical trials and the story of its development as a possible treatment strategy illustrates some of the problems and setbacks involved in drug development.

Initially, mouse models showed that tarenflurbil reduced the production of β-amyloid in brain tissue and prevented learning and memory impairments. Early clinical trials showed that tarenflurbil was safe and well-tolerated. Phase 2 clinical trials were conducted in around 200 patients with mild to moderate AD. Initial results did not show any effect on cognition or function, but further analysis of the results showed that patients with mild AD had a slower rate of decline when on the highest dose of tarenflurbil compared to patients taking a placebo. This led to a large, multicentre Phase 3 trial involving around 1700 patients with mild AD, but no benefit was reported and the development process for this drug was stopped in 2009. It has been suggested that even in the mild stages of AD, the amyloid burden is too great for these drugs to have much effect, so this reinforces the need to be able to diagnose or predict AD at the very early stages of the condition (Prins et al., 2010).

This setback, however, has not stopped research in the area of secretase modulation and several substances that inhibit both β- and γ-secretase are currently in various stages of the development process. Additionally, the activation of α-secretase has been investigated as a possible therapeutic strategy (Lichtenthaler and Haass, 2004).

- What is the theoretical basis of this line of research?

- α-secretase cuts amyloid precursor protein at a site that does not result in the production of β-amyloid. Therefore, in theory, activation of this enzyme could reduce the levels of β-amyloid produced.

Activity 3.3 Alzheimer's research: a scientist at the cutting edge

(LOs 3.1, 3.3, 3.4, 3.5 and 3.6) Allow 30 minutes

In the multimedia map, listen to the audio recording of Professor Martin Rossor talking about current research into finding a cure for AD. Answer the questions that follow each section of the recording.

3.4.4 Targeting tau

The development of treatment strategies that target tau has had less emphasis than those targeting amyloid, but according to some researchers any future therapies should aim to reduce both amyloid- and tau-related pathology (Rafii and Aisen, 2009). Chapter 2 of this book described the formation of neurofibrillary tangles (NFTs) in the Alzheimer's brain containing a hyperphosphorylated form of tau. The presence of tangles throughout the cortex and hippocampus is thought to be related to the severity of the symptoms of AD. So, one possible strategy for halting the progression of the dementia would be to interfere with the aggregation of tau into these tangles.

Methylthioninium chloride (also known as methylene blue and by the brand name Rember®) is a pharmacotherapy that targets hyperphosphorylated tau protein. Methylene blue is a molecule that is sometimes used as a drug for other conditions such as urinary tract infection and is also a widely used histology dye. It is known to interfere with tau aggregation and may also dissociate existing aggregates. Preclinical and clinical studies up to Phase 2 trials have produced promising results in some participants and Phase 3 trials are planned.

Other ways of reducing tau pathology would be to reduce the amount of tau phosphorylation and some substances have been shown to do this. Research is in the early stages for treatments based on this approach.

3.5 Inflammation

3.5.1 Alzheimer's dementia as an inflammatory response

So far in this chapter you have read about various drug treatments that act on the neuronal pathways that may be involved in the development of AD. You have also read in the previous section about ongoing research into treatments targeting levels of amyloid and tau. This section introduces another area of biology, in which the body reacts against injury or an infection to produce an **inflammatory response** (see Box 3.5).

Box 3.5 Inflammation

An inflammatory response is part of the body's immune system which protects against damage or invasion by potentially harmful substances. Inflammatory responses are characterised by the accumulation of cells such as white blood cells around the affected area, which release various chemicals designed to remove damaged tissue or the source of the infection and to promote healing of the tissue. Cells called macrophages surround and engulf dead cells and debris from the site of injury. Typically the area becomes swollen, hot and red during this process (you may have experienced an inflamed spot or boil, for example). Usually the response is short-lived, the source of injury is removed and the tissue heals; this is known as an acute inflammatory response. Some diseases, however, are characterised by a long-term, or chronic, inflammatory response where the response continues indefinitely. A well-known example is rheumatoid arthritis which is a chronic inflammatory disease affecting the joints and other tissues. In chronic inflammatory illnesses, the trigger for the inflammatory response is usually a component of the person's own cells or tissues.

For a long time it was thought that the brain was not susceptible to these inflammatory attacks, as cells and large molecules cannot easily move in and out of the brain due to the blood–brain barrier, a protective barrier of blood vessels and cells (Book 2, Section 3.5). However, it is now known that there can be some movement of inflammatory cells into the brain. More significantly, a type of cell in the brain called **microglial cells** (or microglia) seem to behave like inflammatory cells in that they become activated after neuronal injury and release chemicals similar to those seen in an inflammatory response. They also behave like macrophages and engulf and remove dead cells or parts of cells. Inflammatory responses in the brain are now thought to be important in some neurological disorders, including AD, Parkinson's disease and multiple sclerosis.

Glial cells are supporting cells in the nervous system and have a variety of roles including providing physical support to neurons, controlling the chemical composition of the extracellular fluid, providing nutrients, and providing the myelin coating (Book 1, Activity 2.2) that speeds up transmission along axons. Microglia are the smallest of these glial cells and their main function is to remove damaged tissue and protect the brain against infection.

The theory that an inflammatory response is involved in the development of AD pathology has a long history. Post-mortem studies show that the tissue surrounding amyloid plaques is full of cells and chemicals associated with inflammation, including microglial cells that respond to damaged brain tissue. Much research has been carried out to find out the significance of these observations: for example, how an inflammatory response might be linked to other theories of AD pathology such as the amyloid cascade (Chapter 2). Cell culture studies (Box 2.3) have found that insoluble β-amyloid deposits can initiate some of the chemical pathways associated with inflammation and activate microglia. Furthermore, the appearance of amyloid deposits and microglial cells seems to occur relatively early on in the sequence of pathogenic events in AD, before the appearance of NFTs or of neuron loss (Eikelenboom et al., 2006). Evidence is accumulating that inflammatory reactions may occur in the early stages of AD, perhaps as a response to increased levels of β-amyloid, which is treated as a 'foreign' substance. This entirely normal reaction is perhaps beneficial initially in removing small amounts of β-amyloid, but with increasing levels of the peptide the cycle of inflammation gets out of control and the toxic effects of inflammatory factors contribute to neuronal damage caused by the amyloid cascade. Figure 3.10 shows an adaptation of the amyloid cascade hypothesis to include a contribution to the pathology by inflammatory responses.

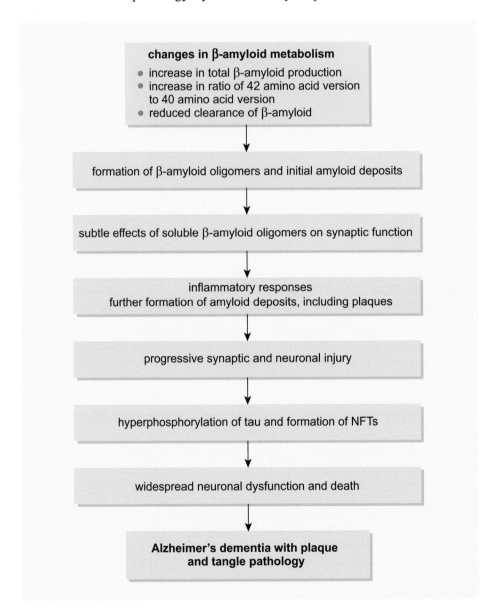

Figure 3.10 Diagram of the amyloid cascade with the inclusion of an inflammatory response contributing to neuronal damage. Adapted from Haass and Selkoe (2007).

The theory that inflammation could play a part in the development of AD pathology has introduced ideas for new areas of therapy. One possibility is the use of non-steroidal anti-inflammatory drugs (NSAIDs), which are commonly used for other long-term inflammatory conditions. A review of multiple epidemiological studies reports a trend towards lower levels of AD among users of NSAIDs for other conditions (McGeer and McGeer, 2007), indicating that the long-term use of NSAIDs may be protective against the development of AD. Some studies in transgenic mouse models of AD (Box 2.2) have shown a reduction in AD pathology after the administration of NSAIDs. Clinical trials in people with mild to moderate AD have, however, been disappointing. It may be the case, as with other therapies, that NSAIDs need to be administered very early in the development of the condition to have any effect.

The other possible area of therapy is that of stimulating the immune responses of the brain in order to remove β-amyloid. Progress with this approach is discussed in the next section.

3.5.2 Developing a vaccine

The idea of a vaccine to protect against Alzheimer's dementia developed from the evidence described above, that inflammatory responses may be involved in the development of the condition. The principle of vaccination is that a small amount of the substance that triggers an immune response is introduced into the body, such that a controlled reaction occurs to the substance which does not cause illness. The idea is that the body is then 'primed' to react more effectively when it encounters the substance on a future occasion. This is known as active vaccination because the body has to actively produce antibodies which remove the substance introduced into the body

Initial experiments were performed in transgenic mice that produce an abnormal form of APP, leading to the development of the pathological features of AD. The mice were injected with the 42 amino acid β-amyloid peptide, with the aim that the immune system would be stimulated to produce antibodies that remove this form of β-amyloid. The experiments seemed to be successful in that young mice given the vaccine developed far fewer amyloid deposits than untreated mice. Furthermore, vaccination of older mice slowed down the progression of the pathology (Schenk et al., 1999).

The success in these early experiments was sufficient to lead to a clinical trial of a β-amyloid vaccine in humans with mild to moderate AD symptoms. Unfortunately, however, some of the participants in the trial developed severe side effects to the vaccine, including inflammatory reactions in the brain, so the trial had to be abandoned. However, subsequent monitoring of participants in the trial has provided some encouraging results. For example, one follow-up study showed that the vaccine caused a reduction in the rate of decline in cognitive performance in a proportion of the participants, as shown in Figure 3.11 (Hock et al., 2003).

There are some reports of new varieties of the β-amyloid peptide vaccine that may be less harmful than the original version. Research is also currently being carried out to develop different

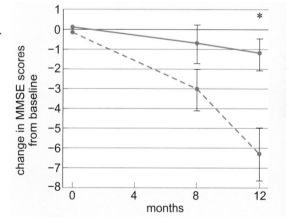

Figure 3.11 The results of an early trial of immunisation with 42 amino acid β-amyloid in AD. Changes in MMSE scores from baseline are shown (mean ± SEM). The solid line shows the cognitive performance over 12 months in participants that responded to the vaccine by producing antibodies against β-amyloid. The MMSE score in these patients declined more slowly than in the patients that did not respond to the vaccine (dashed line). The asterisk denotes a statistically significant difference between the changes in MMSE scores in the two groups.

sorts of vaccine that have fewer risks of side effects. For example, some vaccines are being trialled that are based on the injection of antibodies against β-amyloid. The antibodies interact with β-amyloid and remove it from the brain, without initiating an immune response in the recipient. This is known as passive vaccination because the body does not have to produce the antibodies itself.

Some of these newer vaccines contain **monoclonal antibodies**, which are highly specific towards a particular substance. One such monoclonal antibody, called bapineuzumab, is looking promising. A 78-week study of the effects of this antibody was conducted in patients with mild to moderate AD. Patients were randomised to receive one of three different doses of bapineuzumab or a placebo by intravenous infusion every 13 weeks for up to six infusions. The patients underwent PET scanning to assess accumulation of β-amyloid. The extent of amyloid deposition increased in the placebo group but decreased in the treated groups over the 78 weeks. Relative to placebo, the treatment was calculated to have reduced β-amyloid by 25% (Rinne et al., 2010). Clinical trials are continuing to determine the effects of the antibody on cognitive performance. Preliminary analysis has shown that, in some people with AD, bapineuzumab treatment resulted in a smaller decline in cognitive function over 78 weeks compared with placebo (Prins et al., 2010). This is an area of research that will undoubtedly continue for some years to come.

■ What is the difference between active and passive vaccination?

☐ Active vaccination involves the introduction of a substance into the body that initiates the production of antibodies to remove that substance. Passive vaccination involves the introduction of antibodies into the body that remove a particular substance from the body.

3.6 Vascular disease and Alzheimer's dementia

3.6.1 Evidence for vascular damage in Alzheimer's dementia

Increasingly, the question is being asked whether AD is primarily a vascular disorder with neurological consequences. Some workers in the field (de la Torre, 2009) would say this is no longer a question but an obvious certainty. Others do not go quite this far, but nevertheless claim that vascular abnormalities are a major and essential component of AD, and have a critical role in development and progression of the condition (Cavalieri et al., 2010; Bell and Zlokovic, 2009). What, then, is the evidence for vascular malfunction being linked to AD? A close relationship between AD and malfunction of blood vessels serving the brain has been known to exist for many years. A high-profile contribution to the field is the Nun Study that has been formally ongoing since 1986 in the USA. A community of 678 nuns who live similar simple lifestyles in a religious congregation have been monitored and subjected to post-mortem investigation upon death. Key early findings include the observation that nuns were more likely to exhibit the cognitive signs of dementia two to four years earlier if they not only had AD pathology but also showed evidence of damage from ischaemia (lack of blood supply to a tissue, in this case the brain) (Snowdon et al., 1997). Other epidemiological evidence for an association between vascular damage and AD is found in a different study where only 21% of individuals with an AD diagnosis had pure AD pathology without any other brain abnormalities (Medical Research Council Neuropathology Group, 2001).

■ If the blood supply to the brain is lowered, what general effects would you expect this to have on brain tissue?

□ There would be a reduced supply of oxygen, energy sources and other essential chemicals, and reduced elimination of waste or redundant chemicals.

It is suggested that this deficiency in energy resources available to brain tissue results in a cascade of malfunction that will lead to or contribute to the classical pathology of AD: amyloid plaques, neurofibrillary tangles, and diminished brain size (Perez and Cancela Carral, 2008; de la Torre, 2009).

There is also considerable evidence of malfunction of the blood–brain barrier in AD.

■ You have met the blood–brain barrier before (Book 2, Section 3.5 and this chapter, Box 3.5). Can you recall its function?

□ It forms a barrier between the blood in small vessels serving the brain, and the brain tissue itself. It regulates the movement of chemicals from blood to the fluid that surrounds neurons and glial cells in the brain.

This local fluid environment of the central nervous system is provided by the cerebrospinal fluid (CSF) which is being produced continuously and drained away. Any abnormality of the blood–brain barrier might affect both the drainage of the CSF and removal of unwanted substances from the brain, but it is also possible that access of ions, nutrients and vitamins to the CSF could be affected. In Chapter 2 you learned of the apparent role of β-amyloid in AD, and in the context of damage to the blood–brain barrier, considerable attention is being paid to the possible failure of β-amyloid to be cleared properly from the brain. It is worth noting that a primary characteristic of AD is the deposition of β-amyloid in cerebral blood vessel walls (Bell and Zlokovic, 2009).

There are various ways of explaining the links between vascular damage and AD. For example, vascular changes could initiate the onset of the dementia, or vascular damage could occur alongside the preliminaries of AD such that the symptoms of AD are accelerated. Alternatively, a third factor such as oxidative damage (Table 2.1) may underlie both vascular damage and AD so that they occur in parallel. Whatever the explanation, the view that vascular changes are fundamentally linked to AD is becoming widespread.

You may wonder how this can be reconciled with what you read in Chapter 1 regarding the differences between Alzheimer's and vascular dementia. From a clinical perspective, it is sensible to make the distinctions described in Chapter 1 so that appropriate diagnoses can be made and treatment initiated. But looking to the future, we should keep an open mind and consider that AD is also caused, at least in part, by vascular damage. Conditions such as heart disease, high blood pressure, high cholesterol and diabetes can all cause damage to blood vessels and could contribute to the risk of developing AD. The implications of these links for potential treatments are explored next.

3.6.2 Antihypertensives and statins

Leading on from the previous section, it is worth considering the idea that we could lower the risk of developing Alzheimer's dementia by taking medications that lower blood pressure or cholesterol levels. An obvious place to start looking for evidence that this might be an effective strategy is to look at the epidemiological evidence from people already taking these drugs.

- ■ Can you think of any potential problems with performing these epidemiological studies?

- ☐ Firstly, there are many different types of drug available and they work in different ways. Secondly, in elderly populations, a high proportion of people will be taking more than one type of medication, which introduces other variables. Finally, there will be many other variables involved, such as diet and levels of physical activity.

Nevertheless, many epidemiological studies have been performed and there is evidence that at least some types of **antihypertensives** (drugs that reduce blood pressure) affect cognitive function and reduce the incidence of AD and other dementias (Li et al., 2010, Paran et al., 2010). The findings are complex, however, and there is no clear consensus that antihypertensive treatment reduces the risk of dementia or cognitive decline. Also, the balance of evidence suggests that high blood pressure in mid-life is a risk factor for dementia, but the position in later life is unclear.

Moving on to cholesterol levels, the effect of **statins** (cholesterol-lowering drugs) has been studied intensively in recent years and many epidemiological studies have suggested that statins reduce the risk of AD (reviewed in Jedrziewski et al., 2005). For example, in one study, patients aged over 50 diagnosed with high cholesterol levels were monitored over six years. Those who had been prescribed statins had a 71% lower risk of developing dementia or AD. In another study, patients already on statins were found to have a lower incidence of AD compared to those not taking statins. After 11 months, patients in the statin group had increased MMSE scores, whereas the non-statin group had decreased MMSE scores. However, two recent large RCTs comparing statins with placebo did not show a protective effect on cognitive decline (Shah et al., 2008). Clinical trials in people with AD or at risk of AD are continuing.

To conclude this section, it should be said the most beneficial approach might be to adopt lifestyle changes that lower the risk of high cholesterol levels or heart disease, such as adopting a healthy diet and engaging in regular physical activity. Here we see the overlap of biological factors with wider psychosocial issues.

3.7 Other treatment options

Sections 3.4 to 3.6 have described some of the current areas of research that may lead to future strategies for treating Alzheimer's dementia. You should now be able to appreciate the diversity of the approaches looked at in an attempt to find a cure for this complex condition. There is no space to discuss all of the current research, but two other lines of enquiry deserve a brief mention before concluding the chapter.

Firstly, it has been mentioned above and in the previous chapter (Table 2.2) that diabetes may be a risk factor for AD. Diabetes affects the vascular system, which was discussed in the previous section. The hormone insulin, which is lacking or not used properly in diabetes, is essential for cell function. Trials are currently taking place to assess the effect of insulin, or chemicals that help brain cells to use it properly, on cognitive function in AD.

Secondly, it has been suggested that the hormone oestrogen may be involved as it is known to protect neurons from damage, and that loss of oestrogen after the menopause may be linked to AD. Some epidemiological studies have suggested that oestrogen replacement may delay the onset of AD, but results from RCTs are not consistent so further research is needed in this area (Shah et al., 2008).

Table 3.3 summarises some of the pharmacological approaches to treating AD that are currently being investigated in clinical trials.

Table 3.3 Pharmacological approaches to treating Alzheimer's dementia. (Adapted from Mucke, 2009.)

Approach	Basis of action
Secretase modification	Decreases formation of β-amyloid from amyloid precursor protein
Vaccination with β-amyloid peptides (active vaccination)	Generates antibodies that interact with β-amyloid and remove it from the brain
Vaccination with antibodies against β-amyloid (passive vaccination)	Antibodies interact with β-amyloid and remove it from the brain
Injection of non-specific antibody products	May remove β-amyloid and other proteins and reduce inflammatory processes
Modifiers of tau accumulation	May reduce tau phosphorylation or aggregation
Stimulation of insulin signalling	May replace insulin or overcome lack of response to insulin in the brain
Modulation of oestrogen receptors	Promotes neuroprotective effects of oestrogen
Neuroprotective agents	Stimulates pathways that protect against excitotoxicity

3.8 Final word

In this chapter you have read about the existing drug treatments for Alzheimer's dementia and how they work. You have also seen that the positive effects of these drugs on the symptoms of AD are limited and that they have various problems including unwanted side effects. We have also examined future strategies for treatments based on reducing the brain deposits of amyloid and tau, including the development of vaccines. Finally, the chapter discussed strategies for treatment based on the view that AD is a vascular disorder.

You have seen that the process for developing a drug treatment is lengthy and complex, and sometimes promising results at the early stages are not seen at later stages. It seems unlikely that a 'wonder drug' will be found for AD, but there is a good chance that some of the current research will result in useful pharmacotherapies, at least for some groups of patients. It is possible that future therapies will involve a combination of treatments targeting different aspects of the symptoms and pathology. Researchers are on the whole optimistic about the prospects for effective drug therapies for AD within the next few years.

Throughout this module, however, you have learnt that the treatment of mental illness should not rely on a biomedical approach alone, and AD is no exception to this. There is growing recognition that effective treatment for AD should include non-pharmacological approaches and these will be discussed in the next chapter. We will consider the future of good quality dementia care that includes biological, social and psychological approaches. In addition, we will briefly address the question of whether efforts might best be directed at preventing the development of dementia in the first place.

3.9 Summary of Chapter 3

- Any pharmacotherapy for Alzheimer's dementia must overcome challenges such as compliance and intolerance to side effects.
- The most commonly used drugs are anticholinesterases, which block the breakdown of acetylcholine and therefore enhance cholinergic activity in the brain.
- Memantine is also used, which acts on glutamate receptors to prevent overstimulation of these receptors caused by increased levels of glutamate in AD.
- Antipsychotics act on the dopamine pathway and are frequently used for the non-cognitive symptoms of AD such as agitation.
- There is intense research activity to find new treatments for AD, which involves preclinical research and a lengthy process of conducting clinical trials.
- Research is under way to find new treatments for AD based on reducing levels of β-amyloid and tau.
- The role of inflammation and immune responses in AD is being investigated and potential vaccines are in development.

- AD is thought to be linked to vascular damage, which has consequences for future treatments and preventive measures.

3.10 Learning outcomes

LO 3.1 Describe the physiological mechanisms of action of prescribed drug treatments for Alzheimer's dementia. (KU2, KU4)

LO 3.2 Analyse and interpret evidence shown in graphs or tables to illustrate the efficacy of treatments and therapies for AD. (CS3, KS1, PS1)

LO 3.3 Show that you recognise the difficulties associated with finding effective treatments for AD. (KU4, CS4)

LO 3.4 Explain the theoretical basis for the development of new pharmacotherapies for AD. (KU4, CS1)

LO 3.5 Describe the processes involved in the development of new pharmacotherapies for AD. (KU4)

LO 3.6 Illustrate how the process of advancing scientific and clinical understanding is inevitably associated with setbacks and uncertainties. (CS4, CS5)

3.11 Self-assessment questions

SAQ 3.1 (LOs 3.3, 3.5 and 3.6)

Much effort has been invested in understanding the biological basis of Alzheimer's dementia and research scientists and their funding bodies are committed to finding a cure for this illness. Why will finding and delivering this cure not be straightforward?

SAQ 3.2 (LO 3.4)

A research scientist tells you that their group is investigating a new treatment for AD based on the inhibition of γ-secretase. What is the basis for this line of enquiry?

Chapter 4 Perspectives in dementia care

Claire Rostron

4.1 Introduction

In the first chapter of this book you learnt about memory systems from a psychological perspective, and how this knowledge can inform the diagnosis of dementia, as distinct from the cognitive decline that occurs both in normal ageing and mild cognitive impairment. Having clarified how it is possible to recognise dementia medically in Chapter 1, you have also now discovered that our knowledge of the underlying biological changes in the brain that produce the signs and symptoms of Alzheimer's dementia, in particular, is quite extensive (Chapter 2). However, in Chapter 3 you saw that, where there are gaps in this knowledge, these have hindered the discovery of a cure. In addition, you discovered that the currently available drug treatments for AD are far from ideal. The present chapter will therefore explore the role and value of non-pharmacological alternatives for the treatment and care of individuals with dementia. Because these treatments and therapies do not target the brain changes associated with a particular form of dementia, they have the benefit of being relevant to all forms of the condition. At the start of the chapter we will discuss the contrasting approaches that have so far been used to investigate and make sense of dementia, and ultimately how these shape the approach that is taken to treatment and care. Throughout the chapter we will also evaluate the evidence for the efficacy of the non-pharmacological treatments and therapies discussed.

By the end of this book you should be able to form your own opinion of how it might be possible to care effectively and appropriately for people with dementia, and indeed all mental health conditions, based on a combination of knowledge from biological, social and psychological disciplines.

4.2 Perspectives in dementia care

4.2.1 Putting the brain at the forefront of dementia care

To begin the chapter we shall start with a reminder of the biomedical approach to mental health that you encountered at the start of SDK228 in Book 1, Chapter 1. This approach asserts that all that is important in investigating, and therefore understanding, a particular mental health condition is identifying the underlying brain processes that have gone awry, producing a state of brain functioning that can be clearly classified as 'abnormal'. Using this approach, successfully treating any mental health condition could therefore only be achieved by targeting these abnormal changes in physiological function through the design of pharmacological drug treatments. The development of the anticholinesterases is a classic example of this way of thinking about mental health. However, this perspective on mental health has received very staunch critical opposition from social scientists in particular. In the field of dementia treatment and care, one of the harshest critics of the biomedical approach has been Tom Kitwood, a social scientist from the

University of Bradford, who developed an alternative perspective. We shall examine how this perspective differs now.

4.2.2 Putting the person at the forefront of dementia care

In a seminal editorial paper entitled 'Person and process in dementia', Tom Kitwood (Figure 4.1) argued that, while an understanding of the degenerative brain processes that occur in dementia cannot be ignored, it is vital to also give thought to the social and psychological context of the person in dementia (Kitwood, 1993). That is, we should try to separate the person from the neurodegenerative process.

Kitwood argued:

> Twenty years or so ago, the idea that there might be a social psychology of senile dementia – one which would be crucially relevant to medical and social practice – was scarcely thinkable. When psychiatry had made a probable diagnosis of a primary degenerative condition its task was virtually complete; the afflicted person was to be looked after while the disease process took its inexorable course; medication might possibly help with control of mood and behaviour. Now, however, we know much more about the dementing illnesses in their human context, and some of the gloom which pervaded that earlier understanding seems unjustified.

(Kitwood, 1993, p. 541)

Here, aside from the criticism of the biomedical approach, Kitwood makes two important points that are worthy of our consideration. The first is that *more* can be understood about dementia if we investigate it in the complexity of its human context. The other is that, in so doing, we may end up with a far more positive outlook on the treatment and care of people with dementia.

4.2.3 Person-centred care

The idea of putting the person at the forefront of investigation and understanding in health care (not just dementia, because the application is broader than this) is known as **person-centred care** (PCC). Kitwood's development of the notion of PCC marked a significant turning point in research and health care practice for both physiological and mental health conditions. In the rest of the chapter, you will see for yourself just how significant this change has been for how we investigate, understand and care for individuals with dementia.

Figure 4.1 Professor Tom Kitwood (1937–1998) challenged the biomedical approach to dementia and pioneered the concept of person-centred care.

■ In the quoted passage above, Kitwood talks about understanding dementia in its human context. What term (relevant to a biomedical approach), introduced in Book 1, Chapter 1, would be applied to attempts to understand dementia entirely without reference to its human context, by reducing the focus to events in the brain?

☐ Reductionism.

■ In order to understand the complexity of the human experience of dementia, what form of evidence would we need to take into account?

☐   Subjective evidence.

Indeed, what would be needed to make sense of the personal experience and human context of dementia would be qualitative research methods (Book 1, Box 1.1) because these allow the study of dementia in context without attempting to reduce or control that context in any way. Thus you can see how the choice of method for investigation in mental health is shaped by the perspective that is taken.

Crucially, the notion of PCC as Kitwood developed it, would be considered to be a biopsychosocial approach (also first introduced in Book 1, Chapter 1). He argued that the manifestation of dementia in an individual could be understood by the following equation:

manifestation of dementia = personality + biography + physical health + neurological impairment + social psychology

So, while Kitwood argued against the biomedical approach because of its outright exclusion of social and psychological factors, he did not argue the converse that these factors are *all* that are of importance, and that biological factors are not important. Unfortunately, Kitwood's notion of PCC has been applied in the field of dementia care in particular to refer only to a psychosocial frame of reference; that is, applying the exclusion of biological factors. This split between a biomedical approach and a psychosocial approach will become more apparent as we move on to consider the various types of non-pharmacological therapies, because many of these therapies are termed psychosocial therapies in dementia literature.

4.2.4 Malignant social psychology

Kitwood also developed the idea of **malignant social psychology**. This is the notion that inadequate attention to the social and psychological needs of a person with dementia can actually have harmful effects on the well-being of that person. The concept of well-being was discussed in Book 2, Chapter 4. In Kitwood's view, the neglect of psychosocial needs could be deeply damaging to an individual's sense of **personhood**. Personhood refers to the recognition, respect and trust bestowed upon one human being by others in social relationships (Chenoweth et al., 2009). Malignant social psychology might manifest itself in dehumanising acts by care staff, including labelling and infantilisation. Crucially Kitwood believed that the neglect of psychosocial needs was not due to any malignant intent on the behalf of carers but that it was quite simply a side effect of a rigid adherence to a biomedical viewpoint in dementia care. One practical example of this neglect of the psychosocial needs of individuals with dementia means that some individuals in care homes spend long hours essentially sitting staring at the walls with limited social interaction. This inevitably leads to emotional distress that is often viewed by care staff, intent on following routine, as problem behaviour. That is, it is a 'problem' because it disrupts the care routine.

Labelling occurs when the self-identity and behaviour of a person is affected by the actions of others which are determined by the terms used to classify an individual. Infantilisation refers to treating an individual as if they were an infant.

From this viewpoint therefore, one might best care for individuals exhibiting the behavioural signs of dementia by addressing their psychosocial needs, and not by prescribing antipsychotics (Section 3.3). As Kitwood would argue, the dementing process cannot be denied, but many aspects of the person remain intact and therefore they retain the same psychosocial needs that individuals without a diagnosis of dementia have.

One of the practical outputs of the PCC approach has been the development of an assessment tool to enhance awareness of PCC in the care home setting. We shall turn our attention to this tool now.

4.2.5 Dementia care mapping

Dementia care mapping (DCM) is an observational tool that was developed by Tom Kitwood and his colleague Kathleen Bredin from the University of Bradford Dementia Group (Kitwood and Bredin, 1992). It is based around the core idea of PCC that individuals with dementia are still capable of experiencing a sense of well-being and personhood, despite the neurodegenerative changes, if their surrounding environment is a positive one that meets their social and psychological needs. This idea therefore marries with Kitwood's comment in the quoted passage in Section 4.2.2 that our outlook on dementia, and indeed the subjective experience of dementia, has the potential to be positive if we take into account psychological and social factors.

At the heart of this tool is the idea of assessing the quality of dementia care by taking into account the perspective of the person with dementia. In order to do this, dementia care mapping involves an extensive period of observation of the care environment of a person with dementia in order to capture their experience of care on a daily basis. It is a tool that is used in public care homes, and has been piloted in 2010 for use in an individual's own home, for a variety of reasons in addition to research. These reasons might include quality assurance and identification of the training needs of care home staff. Enabling health care professionals to 'see through the eyes' of the person with dementia has the potential to significantly improve the quality of care for dementia, as one user perspective confirms (Vignette 4.1).

Vignette 4.1 The impact of dementia care mapping

The following was taken from an article in NursingTimes.net (2006):

> 'Dementia care mapping is a very thought-provoking experience', says Fay McKalroy, modern matron in older people's services. 'It means looking through someone else's eyes, which is an easy thing to say but very striking when you actually do it. [...] You begin to realise how small deeds and words have a profound impact on people.'

> Her first experience of care mapping was in a dining room on an old people's ward, where she and a colleague observed a woman's experience of the lunchtime routine. 'We sat quietly in the corner. People were aware of us at first but they forgot we were there within about 10 to 15 minutes.'

'First of all, I was amazed by the level of noise in the room. There was no shortage of staff, and they all came in en masse – very noisily. And they tended to talk over the patients. No one was unkind or unpleasant, but they were all focused on the job they had to do, not on the patients' experiences.'

It was clear the woman they were observing, who had dementia, was not enjoying the mealtime. 'She had fleeting periods of ill-being throughout. She looked particularly distressed at one point because the nurses accidentally forgot to give her her lunch – although they quickly noticed and apologised, and gave her a meal.'

The observations also took in the broader environment. They noticed that the staff gave no thought to who sat where, and whether patients had any choice in the matter. 'We listened to the clients talking about the hospital – which wards they liked and disliked, which staff they liked and disliked. It was extremely enlightening. And it has made me think carefully about every aspect of how I approach every patient. For example, whenever I enter a room or a bed space I try very hard to put all my focus on the person first and the clinical task second.'

DCM is also a process as well as a tool. The process of DCM is to brief care home staff on the procedure and relevance of DCM and to feed back the observational data so that any required changes to care may be acted on. Examples of changes that might be brought about by DCM include the initiation of individualised care planning or changes to an individual's care plan, changes at a care unit level, or identification of gaps in resource allocation and discussion of actions that might help alleviate the negative impact of these gaps.

The DCM tool itself has several components. The first is the recording of positive events and personal detractions. Positive events are defined as the enhancement of personhood in an individual with dementia. Personal detractions are the converse. The number of such events is recorded. In addition, there are 24 behavioural categories that can be coded and well-being is also recorded on a scale of +5 (excellent state of well-being) to −5 (a very negative state of ill-being).

Recently the University of Bradford has worked with the British Standards Institute (BSI) to develop guidelines for the use of dementia care mapping known as PAS 800, *Use of Dementia Care Mapping for Improved Person-Centred Care in a Care Provider Organization – Guide* (University of Bradford/BSI, 2010). These publicly available guidelines outline the benefits for care organisations that use the DCM tool and they are the first guidelines of this sort for dementia care in the UK. However, despite the worldwide uptake of DCM, it is not without its critics.

4.2.6 Criticisms of dementia care mapping

One criticism that has been levelled at DCM is that it is an overly complicated assessment tool (Innes, 2009). The latest edition of the DCM tool at the time of writing is the eighth edition. This edition requires (usually) two mappers covering observations of several individuals in a care environment, at five-minute intervals, for the period of at least one day (though it is usual to do two days). Training in DCM takes four days. Those in support of DCM would argue that the tool needs to be complex in order to undertake a fine-grained analysis of the experience of dementia and dementia care, because this experience is also complex (Edwards, 2010). To do any less than this may well open the DCM up to the criticism of reductionism!

Another criticism that has been levelled at DCM is that it can only be effective when care home staff are receptive to the ideas of social psychology and PCC (Edwards, 2010). In addition, not all individuals are receptive to change, as many studies on the management of change in organisations have shown. Furthermore, staff in care homes may need training and long-term support to enable them to act on the issues that arise from the DCM process (Innes, 2003). An example of such problems arising in the application of the DCM process can be seen later in the chapter during Activity 4.3. On the whole, the demands of caring for someone with dementia are so great that there is little time available to reflect on the job, and what results is a **task-centred** approach, where the focus is on the completion of routine tasks. This can be difficult to overcome although, as Vignette 4.1 shows, it may be possible.

4.2.7 Evaluating person-centred care and dementia care mapping

Chapter 3 engaged you in an evaluation of the biomedical approach to understanding dementia through assessing the efficacy of the drug treatments that have been developed for Alzheimer's dementia. In the same vein, we are therefore left with the question of whether the alternative approach first advocated by Tom Kitwood fares any better in terms of delivering desired outcomes in the care of individuals with dementia. One study in Australia has subjected DCM and PCC to a randomised controlled trial (RCT) allowing a comparison between the efficacy of DCM and PCC and the efficacy of drug treatments.

This study allocated 15 residential care sites in Sydney, Australia to PCC principles only, DCM or care as usual (Chenoweth et al., 2009). It is important to understand here that although DCM was developed as a result of a shift in perspective away from a biomedical approach and towards PCC, the latter can be applied without the need to make use of DCM. That is, the two do not necessarily go hand in hand.

■ What is the purpose of the care as usual condition?

☐ This is the control condition.

■ All 15 sites were selected because they were pre-evaluated and found to be task-centred sites. Why was this necessary?

☐ A task-centred care environment (as described in Vignette 4.1) is not an environment that ascribes to the principles of person-centred care. This was necessary to establish a baseline for the PCC condition in particular.

The study used the Cohen-Mansfield Agitation Inventory (CMAI), which is a measure of agitation and behavioural disturbances in dementia, as its outcome. This was applied at baseline, after four months of intervention or treatment as usual, and again after a further period of four months. In this particular study, both DCM and PCC were found to reduce agitation expressed by residents at the care home sites by a statistically significant amount. However, PCC and DCM did not differ from each other and the authors argue that, given the costs associated with undertaking the training, briefing and mapping process for DCM, PCC would be the preferred intervention.

Activity 4.1 Applying DCM in a care setting
(LOs 4.1 and 4.2) Allow 1 hour

Now would be a good time to go to the multimedia map and view the video taken from the programme *Can Gerry Robinson Fix Dementia Care Homes?* This video gives real life examples of 'problem behaviour', otherwise known as behaviour that challenges, and so may be distressing. The clip also demonstrates the process of dementia care mapping and shows malignant social psychology in action.

You should now be in a position to begin to appreciate the potential that PCC can have in dementia care, and how it represents such a stark contrast to a biomedical approach to investigating and understanding dementia. The rest of the chapter will now go on to discuss other forms of non-pharmacological therapies and interventions that are available for the treatment and care of individuals with dementia. There are many non-pharmacological alternatives available and we have space to discuss only a few. While we progress through the rest of the chapter and evaluate those that have been chosen for discussion, it is important to remember that all of these also subscribe to the general principles of PCC.

To begin our discussion we will focus on behaviour management techniques. However, this term may be a cause for some confusion. Surely PCC and DCM are also 'behaviour management techniques'? The answer to that is 'yes they are'. However, the title 'behaviour management techniques' goes back to the origins of these techniques arising from the ideas of conditioning and reinforcement of behaviour (Book 1, Section 1.3.2). These ideas originated before the concept of PCC. Since the development of PCC by Tom Kitwood, behaviour management techniques have moved beyond thinking about behaviour as occurring only as a product of conditioning and reinforcement, and now recognise that there is a psychological element to behaviour that may be unique to a particular individual. Thus the focus on the person is brought into behaviour management.

4.3 Behaviour management techniques

4.3.1 Taking a structured approach

Behaviour management techniques are targeted at the carers of people with dementia, including both care home staff and relative carers. They take a structured approach to 'problem behaviour', known as the ABC approach:

(A) Observe and record events and situations that activate (are antecedents of) particular behaviours.

(B) Carefully describe the behaviour that occurs.

(C) Identify the consequences of that behaviour.

The key to these techniques is that by identifying the causes and consequences of a behaviour, it can (hopefully) be prevented or at the very least managed more successfully by carers, so that it no longer 'challenges'. The essential aspect of carer training is therefore to enable carers to become more aware of the triggers of behaviour so that these triggers may be avoided.

In the modernised PCC version of behaviour management techniques, the underlying assumption is that the behaviour displayed by someone with dementia is directly related to their relationship (or in some cases the absence of a relationship) with their carer(s), and the constraints of their surrounding environment. The output of behaviour management techniques is to create an **individually tailored care plan**, a care plan that is unique to the individual with dementia.

This all sounds very straightforward. However, like DCM training, the problem with implementing these techniques is one of resources. Within the UK, training in behaviour management techniques might be undertaken by a dementia nurse specialist. One such group of specialist nurses are the 'Admiral Nurses' based in London and funded by the charity 'For Dementia'. However, dementia nurse specialists are in very short supply. Also, while a relative carer may be strongly motivated to learn these techniques, it is often the case that care home staff experience barriers to their motivation and commitment (Figure 4.2).

A reference guide for dementia produced by NICE includes guidelines for the non-cognitive symptoms of dementia (NICE, 2006) meaning that the difficulties of dealing with these symptoms and the lack of a cohesive, practical plan for doing this have been recognised by the UK NHS. These guidelines state the priority of staff training of 'all staff working with older people', and they also mention individually tailored care plans, both of which require a significant degree of commitment and investment. Given this required degree of commitment and investment, what is the evidence that behaviour management techniques have a significant effect on the non-cognitive symptoms of dementia?

Figure 4.2 Many care home staff report feeling low motivation due to poor wages and low levels of commitment by management to the provision of staff training. This may well contribute to a task-centred orientation to dementia care.

We shall explore this evidence in detail now and, while we do so, we will consider the difficulties of conducting research of this nature. It is sadly the case that most research conducted to evaluate the efficacy of so-called psychosocial therapies is of poor quality. These conclusions are not the author's own but those of the experts who have conducted **Cochrane Reviews** on these types of therapies or interventions. Cochrane Reviews are meta-analyses of existing research literature (usually RCTs but other methods are acceptable) undertaken to form a body of evidence on which to base decisions about the effectiveness of health care interventions worldwide. Cochrane Reviews are therefore considered to be authoritative. In the following few sections, you will examine the quality of the evidence available for yourself, in order to understand why such conclusions have been drawn.

4.3.2 Evaluating behaviour management techniques

There are surprisingly few RCTs to evaluate the efficacy of behaviour management techniques for the non-cognitive symptoms of dementia. However, we shall examine one trial, conducted in Kent, UK (Gormley et al., 2001). This study focused on the treatment of aggression, and recruited people with all forms of dementia classified according to ICD-10 (see Section 1.4.1). People with dementia were randomly allocated to either the treatment group or the control group, as is the case with all RCTs. There were a total of 34 participants in the behaviour management condition and 28 participants in the control condition.

In this study, the control condition consisted of carers taking part in four sessions of discussion on a variety of care-related issues conducted over eight weeks. By contrast, the treatment condition was carers taking part in four sessions of training in behaviour management conducted over eight weeks. The precise details of the behaviour management programme are shown in Table 4.1.

Table 4.1 Behaviour management programme. Adapted from Gormley et al. (2001).

1	Avoidance or modification of precipitating factors, such as inactivity, frequent environmental changes or complex tasks
2	Use of appropriate communication techniques (e.g. calm approach and adequate explanation before personal care, use of simple one-step commands)
3	Validation or acceptance of false statements or inappropriate requests made by patients
4	Use of distraction techniques during aggressive episodes

The outcomes of the study were scores on the RAGE scale. The RAGE scale (Rating Scale for Aggressive Behaviour in the Elderly) is a scale assessing behaviours such as verbal outbursts, irritability and uncooperativeness on a maximum scale of 63. Mean RAGE scores after treatment were 6.9 for the behaviour management group and 8.6 for the control group (standard deviation was not reported so it is impossible to get an idea of variability in these scores within the groups). Variability is likely to be high because the difference between the two groups, assessed by inferential statistics (see Box 4.1), was not a statistically significant difference. The assessment of whether an observed difference between conditions, or correlation between variables, is statistically significant is discussed in Box 4.1 using the example of the Gormley et al. study.

Box 4.1 Research Methods: Analysis of data – inferential statistics

The analysis of data in an experiment is achieved in two stages. The first stage, known as descriptive statistics, was discussed in Book 2, Box 1.3. The second stage goes beyond the simple description of a difference between conditions or relationship between variables and allows inference to be drawn from the experimental data. That is: was the experimental hypothesis supported? The statistical analysis of data in this second stage is therefore known as **inferential statistics**.

There are many types of inferential statistical tests and the choice of test depends on such things as the nature of the data (Book 3, Box 3.1), whether the data describe differences or a correlation (Book 1, Box 4.5), and the number of dependent or independent variables in a study (Book 1, Box 2.1).

In the experiment by Gormley and colleagues (2001), the researchers were interested in comparing the RAGE scores between two groups. To do this, they used an inferential statistic called a t-test. A t-test calculates a statistically significant result if the experimental effect of manipulating the independent variable is greater than the chance effect of naturally occurring variation between individuals.

The criterion for determining whether a difference is statistically significant, or not, can be set by the researchers. It depends on the level of risk that the experimenters are willing to take in making the wrong conclusion. A wrong conclusion can take two forms: false positive and false negative. A false positive conclusion would mean that the researchers concluded that the experimental hypothesis was supported when in fact the results were just due to chance variation. A false negative would mean that the experimental hypothesis was rejected, when in fact the results were not due to chance variation. You first met these terms in relation to diagnosis in Book 1, Box 4.7.

The level of risk is expressed as a criterion p value which refers to the probability that the experimental results are due to chance; that is, p = probability. Most researchers within psychology settle on a criterion p value of 0.05. When the p value is expressed in this way, it is a proportional value. This means that a value of p = 1.00 is equivalent to a 100% likelihood that the results were due to chance variation between individuals. Therefore a p value of 0.05 can also be thought of as 5 in 100, or a 5% likelihood that the results occurred because of chance variation. This choice of the critical value of p is a delicate balance between the risk of a false negative and false positive experimental conclusion.

When a p value is calculated by a statistical test, this value is compared with the critical value that was chosen by the experimenters. If the obtained p value is equal to or greater than this critical value, then the results are too likely to have occurred by chance and the experimenters will not infer that the experimental hypothesis was supported by the experimental data.

By contrast, if the p value calculated by the test is lower than the critical value, then the researchers will conclude, or infer, that the null hypothesis (that there will be no significant difference between the experimental and control conditions) can be rejected and that the experimental hypothesis was supported.

As this decision would accept any value lower than the critical value (0.05 in this case), it is usual to see the critical value of p being expressed in the form $p < 0.05$. This is simply stating that the value of p returned by the statistical test must be less than (<) 0.05.

■ Suppose that experimenters have set a critical value of $p < 0.05$ and a statistical test returns a value of $p = 0.08$. Is the experimental hypothesis supported?

□ No. The value of p is greater than (>) 0.05 and p must be less than (<) 0.05 for the experimental hypothesis to be supported.

■ Suppose that experimenters have set a critical value of $p < 0.01$ and a statistical test returns a value of $p = 0.001$. Is the experimental hypothesis supported?

□ Yes; a value of 0.001 is less than a value of 0.01. Therefore the value of p does meet the criterion of being less than (<) 0.01. The experimental hypothesis is supported.

Activity 4.2 Importance of participant characteristics

(LOs 4.3 and 4.4) Allow 10 minutes

Look at the participant characteristics taken prior to treatment from the Gormley et al. (2001) study shown in Table 4.2. Note any differences between the two groups that you think might be worth taking into consideration when drawing conclusions from the study results. Note also your reasons for choosing these differences.

Table 4.2 Participant characteristics recorded at the start of the experiment by Gormley et al. (2001).

	Behaviour management	**Control**
Mean age of patient	75.6	76.3
Mean MMSE score	13.2	13.5
Mean RAGE score	9.4	8.8
Number taking psychotropic medication	20 (out of 34)	16 (out of 28)
Mean age of caregivers	68.9	68.0

On noting the pre-existing difference in RAGE scores, the authors of the study conducted an inferential statistical analysis that can take account of this difference with the critical p value set at $p < 0.05$.

- The p value returned by the analysis of RAGE scores after treatment was $p = 0.071$. Was the experimental hypothesis that there would be a difference in RAGE scores between the behaviour management group and the control group supported?

☐ No it was not.

- Why is this?

☐ A p value of 0.071 is not statistically significant. Therefore the authors cannot reject the null hypothesis because the risk that the results occurred by chance is too great.

Based on this very weak evidence, it is perhaps easy to understand why behaviour management techniques are not in widespread use at present. The benefits shown by the few studies conducted do not appear to justify the costs associated with training. However, that is not to say that the techniques do not work. What will be needed are further carefully designed studies so that evidence can be gathered to support the efficacy of these techniques. However, an important point to bear in mind is that RCTs are not the only method by which one can gather evidence on efficacy, and we shall talk more on this issue later in the chapter.

Unfortunately those studies that have been conducted so far also suffer from the problems associated with undertaking all studies to assess efficacy of non-pharmacological treatments and therapies for dementia. One of these core issues is the selection of appropriate **outcome measures**. Outcome measures are not to be confused with dependent variables. Dependent variables are the data produced by a study that reflect the effect of a treatment or intervention. Outcome measures are the standard by which these study effects are assessed. That is, an outcome measure is very much like a goal to aim for when designing a treatment or intervention. Outcome measures are selected by groups of experts and policymakers.

The British Psychological Society has released guidelines on the selection of appropriate outcome measures for researchers interested in assessing the efficacy of non-pharmacological therapies for dementia (Sperlinger et al., 2004). This guidance was some while in the making, suggesting that even the experts find reaching a consensus on a desirable outcome for dementia difficult.

It may well be that the most appropriate outcome measure for a biological treatment is biological and that the most appropriate outcome measure for a psychological treatment is psychological, and so on. The problem with this approach then becomes one of drawing comparisons across disciplines. The reality of mental health conditions is that they encompass all of these factors.

We have talked specifically here about outcome measures in relation to behaviour management techniques. As we shall see in the rest of the chapter, these issues apply equally to the assessment of all non-pharmacological therapies for dementia.

Activity 4.3 The impact of person-centred care and dementia care mapping in a care setting

(LOs 4.2 and 4.4) Allow 45 minutes

Now would be a good time to go to the multimedia map and watch the second video taken from the programme *Can Gerry Robinson Fix Dementia Care Homes?* The video concerns the outcomes of application of PCC and DCM in a care home environment.

4.4 Reminiscence therapy

Reminiscence therapy, as the name suggests, involves discussing the past. In particular, this includes recalling experiences and events unique to the individual person with dementia, and it is best conducted using prompts such as personal photographs or household objects (Figure 4.3).

Reminiscence therapy can be conducted as a joint therapy between the person with dementia and their relative carer. When this is done, it is believed to enhance the troubled social bond that can exist as a result of the stressful nature of the caring situation.

Reminiscence therapy relies on an intact autobiographical memory, which is part of long-term memory (Section 1.3.2). Most importantly the theory behind reminiscence therapy is that it helps the person with dementia to regain a **sense of self** that can become damaged as a result of the cognitive and non-cognitive changes occurring with this condition. A sense of self refers to an internal knowledge of oneself as a unique individual. When one has an intact sense of self, it is difficult to imagine what the loss of this would feel like, but there is some evidence that sense of self can become altered in dementia (Cohen-Mansfield et al., 2000), particularly from the self-reports

Figure 4.3 Recalling autobiographical memories in dementia helps to regain a sense of self.

of people with dementia (Vignette 4.2). Therefore a therapy that could protect the sense of self would be very valuable indeed.

> **Vignette 4.2 Losing oneself in dementia**
>
> No theory of medicine can explain what is happening to me. Every few months I sense that another piece of me is missing. My life … myself … are falling apart. I can only think half thoughts now. Someday I may wake up and not think at all, not know who I am. Most people expect to die someday, but whoever expected to lose their self.

This frightening experience was well documented in a diary of a dementia sufferer (Cohen and Eisdorfer, 1986) cited in Cohen-Mansfield et al. (2000).

Not surprisingly then, this form of psychosocial therapy is the most common of all the possible psychosocial therapies, meaning that it is the most frequently used to treat the non-cognitive symptoms of dementia. However, a Cochrane Review conducted by Bob Woods and colleagues (Woods et al., 2005) found that an overall evaluation of the efficacy of reminiscence therapy by combining the results of all RCTs conducted on it (a meta-analysis) was almost impossible to complete. This was because most of the studies were small and of poor quality, with many variations in the exact type of reminiscence therapy that was used. In their paper in 2005, Woods and colleagues noted an urgent need for more robust studies so that valid conclusions regarding efficacy could be made. Unfortunately, an update to the Cochrane Review in 2009 by Woods and colleagues did not reach a different conclusion. This was due still to the poor quality of research that has been conducted into this therapy.

Any psychosocial therapy for dementia, however, surely could be considered to have the added benefit that it does not produce side effects such as those experienced as a result of the available pharmacological treatments? But, you would be mistaken to think that this is the case. Although the side effects of reminiscence therapy could never be as severe physically as those of the antipsychotics, it is certainly the case that reminiscence therapy is not side effect free. There can be some strong negative psychological consequences, primarily because not all of an individual's memories of the past are positive.

4.5 SPECAL

SPECAL was originally devised as an acronym to mean 'specialised early care for Alzheimer's'; however, it refers now specifically to an independent charity organisation that delivers training in the management of all forms of dementia for carers.

SPECAL follows a PCC approach to dementia and aims to deliver lifelong well-being to someone diagnosed with dementia through individually tailored care.

Activity 4.4 The SPECAL approach

(LO 4.1) Allow 30 minutes

Now would be a good time to go to the multimedia map and listen to the audio clips of Penny Garner, the founder of SPECAL, talking about the ideas that underpin the SPECAL approach to dementia care and exactly how SPECAL works.

It is not possible to discuss the efficacy of SPECAL as assessed by an RCT, as this form of evaluation has not yet been conducted. However, SPECAL has many advocates who feel very strongly that the approach has helped them to make sense of the person with dementia. A case account of this nature is included in Activity 4.5 shortly, and you can form your own opinion of the weight that this form of evidence should carry.

At the time of writing, SPECAL struggles to establish its credibility in the eyes of academics and policymakers because, it is argued, the approach is unethical. In essence, SPECAL has been accused of advocating lying to people with dementia.

- ■ From your knowledge of SPECAL gained from Activity 4.4, why do you think that SPECAL might be accused of advocating lying?

- □ SPECAL has been accused of advocating lying to people with dementia because it involves misleading them about the reality of their situation by directing them to information stored from the past in their memory.

Activity 4.5 Deborah and Penny evaluate SPECAL

(LO 4.1) Allow 45 minutes

Now would be a good time to go to the multimedia map and listen to the audio clips of Deborah (a carer for someone with dementia) and Penny Garner talking about the SPECAL approach. Deborah gives a carer view of SPECAL, evaluating its success as an intervention for dementia. By contrast, Penny (the founder of SPECAL) addresses ethical issues surrounding the use of SPECAL and discusses the future for SPECAL in terms of evaluating its efficacy.

4.6 Music therapy

In dementia it is suggested that musical memory of tunes that are already known to an individual is spared (Cuddy and Duffy, 2005). However, singing a song or playing a tune on a musical instrument requires working memory to keep track of one's place, so it is not uncommon for people with the condition to lose track while singing or playing. They can be aided in this process by someone singing or playing along with them. This is essentially how **music therapy** for the treatment of dementia works. The benefits of music therapy are thought to arise from the individual with dementia being able to express him or herself through the medium of song, being with others socially, and being heard (Figure 4.4). Music therapy has no prerequisite for specialised musical training or ability for the individual with dementia and the therapy can span diverse cultures. Trained music therapists are registered professionals with the Health Professions Council and work on a piecemeal basis at day care centres or residential care homes.

Figure 4.4 Music therapy gives individuals with dementia the opportunity to express themselves.

Again, as with reminiscence therapy, a Cochrane Review conducted into the efficacy of music therapy found 'no useful evidence due to small, short-term, poorly designed studies' (Vink et al., 2003). However, case studies of individuals suggest that there are clear benefits for people who receive this form of therapy. Vignette 4.3 is illustrative of this kind of evidence.

Vignette 4.3 The efficacy of music therapy as reported by a music therapist

Mrs O'H. was Irish; she had left her home, with her husband and growing family, in Dublin and had travelled to London in the early 1960s. Whilst they struggled at first to find work, they created a life centred around their children and home. Now in her eighties, Mrs O'H. had been suffering from dementia. Over the past couple of years she had gradually begun to find simple everyday tasks such as making a cup of tea or holding a conversation extremely difficult. Her husband had died, and her three children were grown up with families of their own; she lived alone. She began to leave her house, as she had always done in the morning, but instead of buying a paper and possibly some food at the local shop, she would wander through the streets until eventually someone would notice that she was confused and didn't seem to know where she was or what she was doing.

Her family soon became very concerned and alerted her local GP who in turn referred her to a psychiatric day hospital for older adults. During the six months she attended the day hospital, one of the nurses suggested she join the music therapy group as it was speculated that she might enjoy it. Mrs O'H. started coming to the group sessions I ran as part of my job as a music therapist in the hospital. She seemed extremely anxious and confused and showed difficulty in expressing herself in words, However, I realised that when we sung songs, her face lit up, and she began to join in. As she started coming to the group on a regular basis, I was able to notice the songs she liked, and her enthusiasm for singing Irish folk tunes, as well as songs from British/American shows, inspired me to search out a wider repertoire than I had hitherto used before.

She had a strong singing voice, and although she would lose her way in the song, for example by repeating choruses more than once, she was able to be responsive to my accompaniments on the guitar and piano. In between songs she would tell us, as best as she was able, about how she used to make music with her brothers at home in Dublin and how her brothers and father played instruments, and she would sing. Over a period of four months Mrs O'H. appeared to become completely at ease in the group, as though she was in part replicating the music sessions which had been part of the family occasions of her youth. Whilst her short-term memory was poor, she seemed to remember what happened in the group from week to week and that she apparently knew us. Whilst it was difficult for her to express herself verbally, she could articulate the words of songs, and through the making of music we were able to share sometimes moments of humour and sometimes moments of great sadness and loss.

Interestingly, Ardash Kumar and colleagues (Kumar et al., 1999) conducted a study to assess whether any benefits of music therapy in Alzheimer's dementia could be linked to changes in neurotransmitter or hormone levels. They found that music therapy significantly increased the level of the hormone melatonin in people with AD both immediately after a music therapy session and also six weeks after the end of the music therapy sessions, compared with people with AD who had undergone a control therapy. Melatonin is produced in the pineal gland (in the brain) and is associated with the regulation of the sleep/wake cycle. Many people who fly across time zones take melatonin to reduce the effects of jet lag. It is also interesting to note that people with AD experience disrupted patterns of sleep and this could very well be caused by the loss of cholinergic neurons in the brainstem that have been suggested by researchers to play a role in regulating REM sleep (Datta and Siwek, 1997), though this is still a controversial viewpoint. The addition of a possible biological aspect to music therapy should bring to mind the biopsychosocial model once more and the possibility of interactions between factors.

The term 'REM' refers to rapid eye movement. This is a stage of sleep in which rapid and jerking eye movements are made. It is in this stage that dreams are most vivid.

4.7 Cognitive stimulation therapy

4.7.1 Utilising remaining capacities

Cognitive stimulation therapy (CST), as the name suggests, involves a series of sessions aimed at actively stimulating and engaging people with dementia. These sessions also aim to provide an optimal learning environment and the social benefits of being in a group (Spector, 2006). CST was designed by systematically reviewing the literature on the main non-pharmacological therapies for dementia, and the most effective elements were combined and piloted to create the CST programme. The aim of the CST programme is to create an environment where people learn and strengthen their existing resources, thereby functioning at their maximum possible capacity. The overall view of the person with dementia is therefore one of optimism, focusing on what the person can do rather than one of pessimism, focusing on the capabilities that have been lost. Practically speaking, person-centred care is applied through CST by placing members of the CST therapy group into activities according to their interests and capabilities.

4.7.2 Evaluating cognitive stimulation therapy

Cognitive stimulation therapy is in a rather strong position as far as non-pharmacological (psychosocial) treatments go, because it has been subjected to a large RCT to obtain evidence of its efficacy using the same measures used to show the efficacy of drug treatments for dementia. Thus, the randomised controlled trial for CST conducted by Aimee Spector and colleagues (Spector et al., 2006) enables direct comparisons to be made between psychosocial and pharmacological treatment efficacies. The CST trial based the evaluation of its efficacy on the MMSE primarily. (The MMSE was introduced in Section 1.4.2.) The study was conducted over a short period of time, assessing scores one week before the start of therapy and one week after the end of therapy in care home residents (both in full-time residential care homes, and in day care centres). Participants were included in the study if their MMSE score was assessed at 10 or more prior to assignment to groups.

- What stage of dementia were the participants experiencing?

□ All we can say for sure is that the participants were not in the late stage (MMSE score less than 10). As most subjects came from residential care homes, we might conclude that they were not in the mild stage of the illness. However, some participants were in day care and these participants could quite possibly have been in the mild to moderate stages.

CST was delivered over a period of seven weeks and the control group followed the usual activities associated with their care institutions. In some homes this was nothing and in other homes this included activities such as bingo, music and singing, and arts and crafts.

- Why would the difference in activities in care homes in the control group be a problem?

□ The differences in activities would create variability in the results for this group, making it difficult to show a significant effect of CST. This is not a problem if the study results show a significant effect of CST, but if not, this sort of poor control could lead to a false negative result.

■ What is the independent variable in this study?

□ The independent variable is the treatment type (either control or CST). This design is typical of an RCT.

Some of the results of the study are shown in Table 4.3.

Table 4.3 Study results from the randomised controlled trial of CST conducted by Spector et al. (2006) shown as a change from baseline performance.

Efficacy measure	Treatment mean	Control mean	p value obtained
MMSE	+0.9	−0.4	$p = 0.044$
ADAS-Cog	+1.9	−0.3	$p = 0.014$
QoL-AD	+1.3	−0.8	$p = 0.028$

The ADAS-Cog is a measure of cognitive function in AD and the QoL-AD is a measure of quality of life for AD.

■ What do you notice about the change from baseline data for all efficacy measures?

□ All three of the assessments used show a positive change in the CST group and a negative change in the control group.

There were significant differences between the CST group and the control group in all three measures, at the end of the study. Therefore, despite the problems associated with the control group, a significant beneficial effect of CST could still be shown. However, although this piece of research has achieved a level of design and control comparable to the RCTs conducted to evaluate the efficacy of pharmacological interventions for the treatment of dementia, many other studies have not. This raises the question of whether it is necessary to evaluate so-called psychosocial therapies in this way by a rigorous, objective process of control. This process essentially ignores the very foundations of psychosocial therapies within the discipline of social psychology, where context should be embraced in all its complexity rather than reduced and controlled to make sense of it. As an example, qualitative observational techniques that do not involve manipulation of the independent variable via researcher allocation to groups might perhaps be a more valid method of assessment for these particular health care interventions.

4.8 Defining clinical significance in dementia

The biggest problem facing the evaluation of any therapy for dementia, including pharmacological interventions, is that there is no clearly defined magnitude of change that is considered to be clinically meaningful in assessing treatment benefits. In a recent paper on this issue, Frank Molnar and colleagues (Molnar et al., 2009) have argued that it is essential that outcome measures are found that reflect real-life improvements that have value to people with dementia and their caregivers. This point may seem obvious: of course it should be the case that health care interventions have value to the people that they are designed to care for. Often in RCTs for example, results are shown to be statistically significantly different between treatment and control groups. But what does this actually mean? Statistical significance (discussed in Box 4.1) is only a mathematical phenomenon. Clinically significant differences on the other hand reflect the effect of an intervention that is large enough for people with dementia, their carers or their physicians, to notice an observable benefit. Therefore, the important point to note is that statistically significant differences might not actually be clinically significant and vice versa.

Clinical significance is a very important concept for pharmacological treatments for dementia; in particular, because it enables an informed cost–benefit judgement to be made when deciding whether to start prescribing a drug, and more importantly, whether to continue using a drug when the severe side effects that can occur become apparent. Meanwhile there is a very mixed opinion on what a clinically significant outcome would be for someone with dementia, at least in terms of deciding on a standard and objective definition and so, in most studies, the choice of definition is experimenter opinion only (Molnar et al., 2009).

However, taking into consideration the notion put forward by Molnar and colleagues that interventions for dementia should have value to those being cared for, what are the possibilities of obtaining this value judgement both on behalf of, and perhaps directly from, people with dementia? One study shows that this is indeed entirely possible (Box 4.2).

Box 4.2 Research Methods: Qualitative methods in dementia research – obtaining views on care from people with dementia

Claire Bamford and Errollyn Bruce (Bamford and Bruce, 2000) conducted a study to assess the views of people with dementia about the desired outcomes of their care. This study used a method known as therapeutic group work which involved a series of scheduled formal and informal discussion sessions with people with dementia to access their opinions. Group sessions were chosen because it was believed that these would place a reduced pressure on each individual with dementia to respond to every question if they couldn't understand, or to respond to particular questions. Furthermore, it was argued that the amount of data that could potentially be accessed was greater in a group because sharing experiences might help to trigger memories.

Participants were selected from a resource centre for older people that provided residential care and day care, and chosen by centre staff for inclusion in the study if they felt that the individuals concerned would be able to follow and contribute to the discussion. Consent was obtained verbally and behaviourally rather than in a written manner. This means that each individual was approached by a member of the research team and asked to take part, and that all individuals were free to come and go from the discussion sessions as they pleased.

Discussion was facilitated by two members of the research team and a community psychiatric nurse, using a themed topic guide and a vignette. Themes in the topic guide included the following:

- coming to day care and residential care
- types of help received at home
- the experience of being helped
- help that might be needed in the future
- letting people know how you feel about help.

The vignette was as follows:

"Jack is 80 and lives alone. He's not keeping on top of the cooking and cleaning these days and doesn't see much of other people. When he had a fall recently, he was alone for hours without any help".

The participants were asked to consider the following questions:

- What do you think should be done about Jack?
- How might Jack feel about getting help?
- How could we find out how Jack is getting on?
- What if he got worse and kept falling over, what should be done about him then?

Discussions were recorded using a tape recorder and transcribed to collate any themes that emerged. The published paper reported a subsample of comments that individuals made about their experience of care and the theme associated with those comments (shown underneath each set). For example:

I've gained company for a start and I think that's a big thing. I think you can get morbid when you're on your own for so long. Especially if it's bad weather, you can't get out.

Theme: service users value the chance for social integration.

There's nowt wrong about the place (the resource centre) don't get me wrong. But you do get a bit bored.

Theme: service users value having access to meaningful activity and stimulation.

I felt I was going to die myself, because I felt that way. Giving in. I were sick of being like I were. I felt as though I were putting on everybody and I can't stand that. I'd rather give than take off anybody.

Theme: some service users found it hard to accept care as it threatened their sense of self-esteem and their personal identity.

Service users did not identify improvements in cognitive functioning or a reduction in the frequency of 'problem' behaviours as desired outcomes of services. Furthermore, it was clear from the study that outcome measures such as admission to long-term care were problematic, as some individuals highly valued the chance for social interaction that came from being in the care facility. Service users also valued having a sense of autonomy which is not accurately captured by outcome measures such as functional ability, self-care, mobility and continence. What they actually valued was perceived control that allowed a sense of independence and choice in their daily existence. Therefore, what this study identified was a huge mismatch between typical outcomes selected to assess the impact and efficacy of treatments and health care interventions for dementia, and what people with dementia actually wanted from their treatments and interventions.

Thus we might ask ourselves whether the future of dementia research should further establish such qualitative techniques for use as outcome measures, as opposed to what has so far been a rigid adherence to quantitative measures. There are many who argue that this kind of shift in perspective for research methods also has the potential to improve our outlook on dementia care (Gibson et al., 2004).

4.9 The future of dementia care

In February 2007 the UK Alzheimer's Society published the results of a significant body of research into the prevalence and economic cost of dementia in the UK. This report was called 'Dementia UK: The Full Report' (UK Alzheimer's Society, 2007). The overall conclusions of the report were that, despite some instances of best practice, the care pathways for people with dementia in the UK are failing. Overall, the combination of care by the health and social care services is piecemeal and very poorly understood by many people who use the services. As a result, there is a large degree of regional variation in the quality of care available and many people are unable to access the care that they are entitled to, and would benefit from. For example, only one-third of people with dementia were estimated to have contact with the specialist services that they need.

Along with this problem, which is a direct result of the division of services between the NHS and social services, and divisions within each of these services themselves, there has been the added problem of poor government commitment to funding basic research and health care provision for dementia. For example, in 2007 annual public spending on dementia research was only 15p per citizen in the UK compared with 66p per citizen in the USA. However, in the UK the amount spent annually on research on dementia by charities was estimated to be approximately 5.8p per citizen compared with 3.7p per citizen in the USA (UK Alzheimer's Society, 2007).

You should now be able to form your own opinion of the sort of research that will be required to improve the quality of care for people with dementia. The future of biomedical research was discussed in Chapter 3 and you should consider that it will be invaluable if a cure or effective preventive treatment can be identified in the coming years. For now, however, the current chapter should have equipped you to understand that research that is distinctly not of a biomedical nature also has the significant potential to enhance the experience of dementia care, as indeed Kitwood argued (Section 4.2.2). However, in line with our discussions, the most pressing issue is development of, and agreement on, outcome measures. Indeed, one of the key findings of the report for the Alzheimer's Society was that valid outcome measures must be developed as a key priority for intervention research.

This report is, thankfully, not the end of the story. In February 2009 the Department of Health in the UK issued a policy document entitled 'Living Well with Dementia: A National Dementia Strategy' which was released along with £150 million of public money to implement the strategy identified in the 2007 report (UK Department of Health, 2009). Some of these targets for improvement have been discussed in this book and the relevant ones for our purposes are shown in Table 4.4. At the very least, there is now some hope for the future.

Table 4.4 Some objectives (10 of a total of 17) from the UK dementia report (UK Alzheimer's Society, 2007).

1	Improving public and professional awareness and understanding of dementia
2	Good-quality early diagnosis and intervention for all
3	Good-quality information for those with diagnosed dementia
4	Enabling easy access to care, support and advice following diagnosis
6	Improved community personal support services
8	Improved quality of care for people with dementia in general hospitals
11	Living well with dementia in care homes
13	An informed and effective workforce for people with dementia
15	Improved assessment and regulation of health and care services and of how systems are working for people with dementia and their carers
16	A clear picture of research evidence and needs

However, the challenge will be to efficiently channel the resource that is available to provide the most benefit to the most people.

4.10 Financial and ethical considerations

So far in this book we have looked at emerging developments in diagnosis and pharmacotherapies and in the present chapter we have discussed a range of non-pharmacological approaches that are being used to help people diagnosed with dementia. What we have not yet done is to discuss how delivery of these interventions could be improved, and there is certainly very considerable scope for improvement. Society finds it hard to find suitable frameworks for supporting what is a very diverse group of individuals: they differ in financial status, social and cultural expectations, family/friend relationships, in the variety of dementia types, comorbid conditions, and genetic or other biological differences. Added to this, the needs of those with mild dementia are very different from those with the advanced condition. Strategies are being introduced in the UK to try to improve care, and the National Dementia Strategy has been discussed above. Now we consider an example of how a part of this strategy can be implemented.

At the start of this book we discussed prevalence figures for Alzheimer's dementia, but these are estimated figures. They are based on evidence from multiple sources including many live studies and post-mortem studies, and they don't match the number of individuals who actually have a diagnosis of AD. The number of diagnosed individuals is much lower, and there is an acknowledged need to raise this so that more people receive care – but how? From the estimated prevalence figures, it is possible to estimate how many cases there should be in a city or region, assuming you know how many people live there. Using data from current records of patients, it is possible to compare the current number of recorded dementia cases with the estimated number, and calculate the rate of diagnosis. Unfortunately, the rate is rather low and for dementia as a whole, in 2009, it was around 40%. Strategies therefore need to be implemented to increase this rate and, in Scotland for example, there are plans to raise the diagnosis rate by GPs to a target of 61% by March 2011. The specific measure used is the number of individuals included on the Dementia Register.

Activity 4.6 Improving diagnosis

(LO 4.4) Allow 30 minutes

Figure 4.5 shows diagnosis rates in regions administered by different NHS authorities in Scotland (NHS Boards) and the extent to which, between March 2007 and 2009, they were below the March 2011 target. Record your answers to questions (a)–(d) below.

(a) What general conclusions can tentatively be drawn from the data in Figure 4.5?

(b) What benefits might there be for patients in the target being achieved? Be as specific as you can, but a sentence or two should be sufficient.

(c) What drawbacks might there be for the National Health Service in Scotland? A short answer will be sufficient.

(d) Just having a target for improvement does not guarantee that it will be met. From what you have read in this book and other parts of SDK228, can you suggest one or two changes that might help the target to be met?

One obvious omission from the discussion so far is the issue of cost. Will the costs of extending care and diagnosis procedures be high or affordable? Full discussion of this is outside the scope of this book, but there are some key points that should be made. From the discussion in Chapter 3 you will know

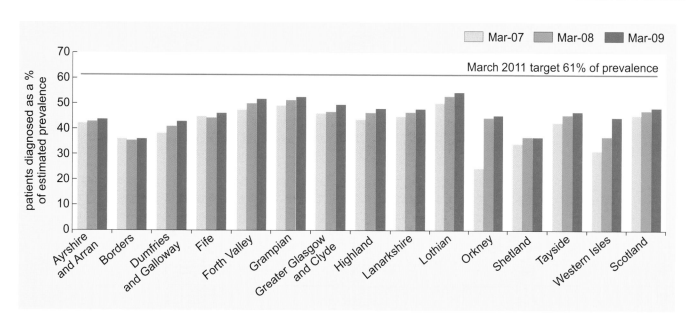

Figure 4.5 Diagnosis rates in Scotland.

that the availability of pharmacological therapies for Alzheimer's dementia via the NHS in the UK at the time of writing (2010) is limited although NICE have issued draft guidelines to amend this. The decision that led to this was based on a calculation that took into account the efficacy of the therapies, their price and the potential number of patients that could be treated. A consequence of the restriction is that a smaller proportion of patients currently gain access to the drugs in the UK than in other Western European countries. This is because, in other countries, the assessment of efficacy and cost versus benefit is different. In turn, this raises the question of what the position will be when newer therapies become available. We can expect a variety of ethical issues to arise. For example:

- To what extent is it ethical for a developed country to restrict access to therapies that comparable countries consider an essential part of care?

- To what extent is it ethical to insist that patients fund certain parts of their care (care home or personal care charges, for example), but erect barriers to prevent them paying for other elements (such as therapies not funded by the NHS)?

- To what extent is it ethical for social care or health care professionals to advise patients on how to get around administrative barriers to obtain the best health care for their personal needs? Should it be dependent on who is employing the professional?

There are no easy answers to these questions, but questions of this type will arise increasingly as the options for diagnosis and treatment expand and we become more conscious of health care standards and options in other developed countries. Behind some of the questions lie the difficulties of integrating the relevant influences that arise at different geographical levels. For the UK, the international dimension of treatment is further illustrated by the fact that medicines are manufactured across the world by international companies of all sizes, medicines are traded across the world, residential homes may be operated by non-UK companies, and the health and social care professionals supporting patients may have trained in countries outside the UK. By contrast, dementia is a personal problem for patients, family and friends, health and social care are delivered according to national and local policies, and support groups usually rely on volunteers working at a local level. Finding social and economic frameworks that are 'fair' to all seems unlikely to become any simpler in the near future.

Another significant ethical issue concerns the position of 'voluntary' carers – family members and friends who care for people with dementia. Their status in society is starting to be discussed more extensively, and there is debate concerning the obligations of employers to put in place support schemes and flexibility regarding working arrangements and leave of absence. Although such things may be some way off, at the very least discussions have now begun.

4.11 Shifting focus: targeting prevention

One might briefly wonder, however, given the barriers to implementing the required improvements that have been identified in the care for individuals with dementia, whether our efforts might best be directed at investigating and understanding the prevention of dementia. Several possible risk factors for dementia have been discussed throughout this book including age, genetics, heart disease and level of physical activity to name a few. What we have not yet discussed is the strength of the research indicating that the slogan 'use it or lose it', in terms of mental stimulation of the brain, may actually be the case.

Considering the idea of 'use it or lose it', or, more academically stated, the effects of cognitive exercise, fits with the general theory of this chapter that attention to the psychological and social needs of an individual can have very positive consequences for the expression of signs and symptoms of dementia. After all, if this is the case, why cannot attention to the psychological and social needs of an individual help to *protect* that person against the development of dementia in the first place?

There has been a vast amount of research into this issue alongside the idea that physical activity, as well as mental activity, may be protective (MacKinnon et al., 2003). However, the jury remains undecided. Unfortunately there are many problems associated with conducting research on this issue, and one of the most salient of these is being unable to demonstrate causality.

It could, for example, be the case that a decline in mental activity ('using it') is an indicator rather than a cause of cognitive decline ('losing it'). A recent meta-analysis (Valenzuela and Sachdev, 2009) included seven RCTs assessing the question of whether cognitive exercise can prevent the onset of dementia. The analysis found a very significant effect (the value of p was considerably lower than 0.05 at $p = 0.006$) but the authors noted problems identifying suitable RCTs to include. This was because there was no agreed definition of what it was that should constitute the independent variable 'cognitive exercise'.

In conclusion, Valenzuela and Sachdev noted that, despite the apparently strong effect shown in their meta-analysis, the crucial study showing that cognitive exercise (or indeed physical exercise) prevents dementia has not yet been conducted. Thus research in this field is fraught with some of the same difficulties as research that assesses the efficacy of health care interventions.

4.12 Medicalisation versus construction of dementia

At the start of SDK228 two contrasting approaches to investigating and understanding mental health were presented to you. These were the biomedical model and the biopsychosocial model. Throughout each of the books you have seen how these approaches can be applied generally within mental health but also specifically to the study of mood and well-being, addiction and in this final book, dementia. Now, at the end of SDK228, you should understand the prescriptive role that these models play in determining the treatments and care that are available worldwide for mental health conditions. But what have we learnt about the usefulness and limitations of these two models? Let us examine this question by returning to the context of dementia care.

Perhaps more so than the other mental health conditions we have discussed in SDK228, dementia has undergone a rigorous process of what social scientists would call **medicalisation**. This term essentially means that a biomedical approach has been applied to make sense of the experience (Innes, 2009). By this approach, dementia can be nothing other than a disease, an approach that has led to the development of pharmacological treatments such as the anticholinesterases and memantine (Chapter 3), and that limits the focus of research to the neurobiology, or neuropsychology of the person with dementia (Cotrell and Shultz, 1993). This approach subscribes wholly to the concept of the brain–mind first presented in Book 1, to the ignorance or exclusion of other factors such as the psychosocial context of the individual with dementia. Such an approach can trace its roots back to Kraepelin and his concept of disease classification, and to the historical origins of the field of psychiatry (Book 1, Chapter 4).

In one sense the medicalisation of dementia may be a good thing because it allows individuals with dementia and their carers to hold out hope for a cure (Innes, 2009). In addition, this view may bring with it a sense of order and legitimacy to dementia care for those affected by dementia (Lyman, 1989). And, as we have seen throughout SDK228, a biomedical approach continues to be dominant in some components of the health care system. Indeed, one report states that it also dominates government and public interest, as well as funding for research, because 'policymakers and funders are not concerned about the care of people with dementia today but are constrained by the more politically gripping agenda of a cure for tomorrow' (Fox, 2000).

On the other hand, in dementia care, we have in the present chapter examined the rival view limiting focus to the psychosocial aspects of dementia known as **social construction**. This view would argue that dementia is a socially constructed phenomenon. That is, that society uses the label 'dementia' to classify individuals as 'abnormal' when in actual fact their experience of dementia is to a large extent determined by the constraints of their external environment and, to a degree, the interactions their caregivers have with them.

Focusing on the psychosocial needs of a person with dementia has to its credit the placement of the individual at the centre of dementia care and also research. It has contributed to an understanding of the subjective experience of dementia and dementia care, and helped make sense of the impact that dementia can have on the sense of self and personhood, all of which we have discussed in the current chapter. However, all these goals were the aims of Tom Kitwood when he criticised the biomedical approach and suggested a biopsychosocial perspective. Despite his clarity on this issue, his original message has sometimes been lost as psychosocial approaches founded on his original notion of person-centred care often completely ignore the contribution of biological factors in mental health. This relationship between all of these different perspectives can be seen in Figure 4.6.

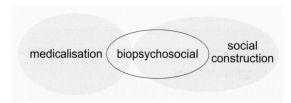

Figure 4.6: The relationship between different perspectives relevant to dementia care.

So, let us end this book by considering what a biopsychosocial approach to dementia care might look like in practice. One article (Boustani et al., 2007) has suggested the following:

1   A feasible dementia identification and diagnosis process including a reliable tool for periodic needs assessment and evaluation of ongoing therapy.

2   Pharmacological and psychosocial interventions that prevent or reduce the family caregiver's psychological and physical burden.

3   Self-management tools to enhance the patient and the caregiver skills in managing dementia disability and navigating the health care system.

4   Pharmacological interventions for care recipients that target the cognitive, functional, and behavioural and psychological symptoms of dementia such as:

   (a) case management and coordination with community resources including adult day care, respite care, and support groups

   (b) modification of the patient's physical home environment to accommodate dementia disability

   (c) an increasing focus on palliative care needs as the illness progresses, including advance care planning, attentive management of pain and other symptoms, avoidance of burdensome and undesired medical treatments, and eventual discussion of referral to hospice.

Therefore, unfortunately, we may still have some way to go. But at least the goal is becoming clearer and a biopsychosocial approach applied to mental health care may well be achievable, though this depends very much on the willingness of the disciplines to work together.

4.13 Final word

Throughout SDK228 there have been indications of how an integrated biopsychosocial approach might be successfully achieved either in research or in the practical aspects of the delivery of care for mental health. As we now reach the inevitable point of a conclusion to SDK228, you should now find yourself equipped with the skills and information that will be necessary for you to answer the following two salient questions:

1   Is an integrated biopsychosocial approach to investigating and understanding mental health worth achieving?

2   If so, how might it be achieved?

4.14 Summary of Chapter 4

- A biomedical perspective on dementia suggests that dementia is a medical condition that requires pharmacological treatment.

- Tom Kitwood criticised this approach to investigating and understanding dementia and developed the notion of person-centred care.

- Person-centred care was developed as a biopsychosocial perspective because it argues for attention to the psychological and social needs of an individual with dementia, but it does not deny the importance of the neurodegenerative process.

- The original biopsychosocial concept of PCC has been used by health and social scientists to devise psychosocial interventions for dementia. These are aimed purely at the psychological and social needs of the individual with dementia, which is how they acquire their name.

- There are a vast number of psychosocial interventions for dementia but many of these do not have strong evidence for their efficacy, due to poorly designed studies. Future research will need to address this situation.

- A key difficulty in evaluating efficacy of dementia interventions is the lack of agreed outcome measures that can be used to decide that an intervention works or does not work.

- Typically, randomised controlled trials have been conducted as a method of efficacy evaluation, but these have their historical roots in the biomedical model because they originated as a means of testing drug treatments.

- Qualitative research suggests that it is possible to obtain value judgements from individuals with dementia concerning the outcomes that they desire from health care interventions. Future research will be needed to develop these methods into agreed outcome measures.

4.15 Learning outcomes

LO 4.1 Describe the importance of, and distinction between, task-centred care and person-centred care. (KU3, CS5)

LO 4.2 Explain the relative contributions of quantitative and qualitative methods used to obtain evidence for the efficacy of psychosocial therapies for dementia. (KU5)

LO 4.3 Analyse and interpret evidence from experiments shown in graphs or tables to illustrate the efficacy of psychosocial therapies for dementia. (CS3, KS1, PS1)

LO 4.4 Show that you recognise the limits of current knowledge for treating and caring for someone with dementia. (CS4)

LO 4.5 Show that you recognise the distinct contributions from and need for interdisciplinary research between biological, psychological and social disciplines. (KU3)

LO 4.6 Explain the theoretical basis of psychosocial therapies for dementia. (KU4)

4.16 Self-assessment questions

SAQ 4.1 (LO 4.1)

What is the core aspect of person-centred care that makes it so different to a biomedical perspective?

SAQ 4.2 (LO 4.2)

Why might randomised controlled trials not be appropriate for the assessment of psychosocial interventions for dementia?

SAQ 4.3 (LO 4.4)

Suppose that you are on a panel of experts reporting to the UK government on whether training at a national level in behaviour management techniques is worth the cost of delivering these techniques. What would your report say?

SAQ 4.4 (LO 4.5)

Although much effort has being directed towards finding a pharmacological cure for Alzheimer's dementia, one has still not been identified. While this effort continues, what is the value of psychosocial therapies?

Answers and comments

Answers to SAQs

SAQ 1.1

This information can be found in incidence rate tables. The chance of a healthy and dementia-free 80-year-old developing Alzheimer's dementia in the following year is about 3% (Table 1.1).

SAQ 1.2

The medial temporal lobes and, specifically, the hippocampus are believed to play a role in the processing of semantic and episodic (declarative) memories.

SAQ 1.3

Frontotemporal dementia causes changes in personality and emotional management that may result in unexpected aggressiveness and/or disinhibited behaviour, as illustrated by Morag (Vignette 1.3a). Alzheimer's dementia, on the other hand, typically causes significant memory impairments, as illustrated by Filip (Vignette 1.2).

SAQ 1.4

The data suggest that the current concept of MCI does not capture the full spectrum of the disorder. There is, for instance, evidence that up to 44% of individuals who have received a diagnosis of MCI at their first visit to clinic were estimated to have returned to normal a year later (Ritchie, 2004; Ganguli et al., 2004). This suggests that MCI may be reversible and may not therefore be a useful diagnostic concept.

SAQ 2.1

The researcher should use an fMRI scan and look for a difference in activity in the area of interest before and during the learning task. Ideally, the results should be compared with similar scans obtained from a person without AD. You may remember from Book 3, Box 2.2 that PET can also be used to investigate activity, but in this chapter PET is described in the context of looking for distribution of a substance.

SAQ 2.2

Until very recently, the pathological changes could only be seen at post-mortem, by which time the dementia is usually at a very advanced stage. Comparisons between different people after death is very difficult as there are so many other factors involved (age, other illnesses, etc.). Also the existence of three different pathological hallmarks (neuron loss, amyloid plaques and NFTs) makes it difficult to investigate the effect of one of these on the occurrence of symptoms.

SAQ 2.3

The main component of amyloid plaques is β-amyloid and of NFTs is tau protein. The β-amyloid in plaques is predominantly of the 42 amino acid version, which is usually only found in small amounts in neurons. The tau protein in NFTs contains an abnormally high number of phosphate groups and therefore is ineffective at binding to and stabilising microtubules.

SAQ 2.4

The genes that have been identified as associated with familial early onset AD show a causal link between the gene and the development of AD pathology. The presence of the gene results in a high probability of developing the dementia. By contrast, the genes associated with late onset AD increase the risk of developing the dementia by a small amount, but the link between gene and pathology is less defined. There are other factors involved in the development of late onset AD, which at current levels of knowledge are impossible to replicate in an animal model.

SAQ 3.1

The links between the various biological changes that can be measured in Alzheimer's dementia and the symptoms of the condition are currently not fully understood. The relationship between them would help us to understand which biological change should be targeted in the search for a cure. There are also difficulties associated with developing drug treatments of any kind, such as finding a well-tolerated drug that can be administered in a manner that would be easily managed in someone with AD. You might also have mentioned the lengthy and costly process of drug development.

SAQ 3.2

γ-Secretase is one of the enzymes involved in the production of β-amyloid from amyloid precursor protein. In theory, blocking the enzyme should reduce the levels of β-amyloid produced in the brain, and therefore reduce the impact of β-amyloid on the progression of the dementia.

SAQ 4.1

Person-centred care argues for attention to the psychological and social needs of a person with dementia. This is in direct contrast to a biomedical approach, which does not consider these needs but instead focuses on the biological aspects of dementia.

SAQ 4.2

RCTs were developed to evaluate the efficacy of pharmacological treatments, so they have been developed from a biomedical perspective. As a result of this, RCTs seek to reduce and control the factors under study while qualitative methods embrace the complexity of context. Given that psychosocial interventions are founded on this viewpoint, it would seem appropriate to evaluate them using qualitative methods.

SAQ 4.3

Your report should indicate that the studies evaluating the efficacy of behaviour management techniques have not been well designed and do not find significant effects, so they do not justify the cost of training at present. More research will be needed to address this problem, and it is possible that this research should include qualitative studies assessing the impact of behaviour management techniques, rather than RCTs.

SAQ 4.4

Although much effort has been directed at finding a cure, while it remains elusive there is still a very large number of individuals experiencing dementia who need appropriate care. Psychosocial interventions have the potential to deliver benefits that are, at the very least, equal to those provided by currently existing pharmacological treatments.

Comments on activities

Activity 1.1

Table 1.2 presents data from other regions with similar levels of development to Sub-Saharan countries (i.e. high mortality rates, indicated by the letter D). North Africa and the Middle East is one example. Compare their prevalence rates for dementia: are they similar or different? If countries with similar levels of development to Sub-Saharan countries have different rates of dementia, then the lower rates of dementia shown in Sub-Saharan countries must be caused by other factors. High mortality in itself does not explain the differences as the data are expressed as a percentage of dementia cases amongst those who have survived into these age groups. Note that apart from age, gender and geographical differences, there have been many lines of investigation into factors that might influence the incidence of AD specifically, such as the role of genes and environmental factors, which could explain some of the differences found in Table 1.2. You will read more about these other risk factors in Chapter 2.

Activity 2.2

A benefit of lesion models might be that the researcher can target the specific area of interest in the brain. In chemical lesioning, a precise amount of the chemical can be delivered to a specific area or group of cells. Drawbacks might be that surrounding areas of the brain could also be affected, or the chemical could diffuse away from the area of interest. Researchers also need to be cautious about inferring normal function from damaged brain function.

Benefits of genetic models are that human genes can be studied and the progression of the disorder can be studied from its earliest stages in a relatively short space of time. On the other hand, the models are quite time-consuming to establish and the gene may be expressed differently in different species.

As a general point, a problem with all animal models is that biological processes may differ from those seen in humans, so researchers need to be cautious in extrapolating results from one species to another. You may also have considered ethical issues involved in animal experimentation, particularly where harm might be caused to the animal. Some people find the whole area of genetic research in particular unacceptable.

Activity 2.5

Benefits could include:

- greater understanding of the pathology and the biological processes involved

- new areas of therapy such as genetic modification or drugs targeting the products of abnormal genes

- genetic testing to identify at-risk individuals or families

- greater knowledge of genetic risk to inform genetic counselling for affected families

- personalised medicine in the future, for example providing treatment or preventive measures to those people with particular genetic profiles.

Activity 4.2

The behaviour management group actually had slightly higher aggression scores as measured by the RAGE when compared with the control group at the start of the study (this is a rather unfortunate consequence of the random allocation to groups). This means that any desired positive effect of behaviour management on aggression scores would have to overcome a pre-existing negative difference, making it less likely that a significant effect of behaviour management could be found.

Activity 4.6

(a) General conclusions are:

   (i)   There seems to be a trend towards slightly increased diagnosis rates over the period studied across most of the NHS Boards.

   (ii) There seems to be a difference between the diagnostic performance of different Boards, with some closer to the March 2011 target than others.

   (iii) The diagnosis rate does not seem to have fallen in any Board over the period studied.

   (iv) Some Boards seem to have improved more than others over the period covered, with the biggest rises seen in Boards with relatively low rates in 2007.

(b) The new target may seem to represent a modest improvement, but should bring several thousand more individuals to the attention of the health care system. Following initial diagnosis, the patient should then have access to specialist diagnosis, management and support from a variety of services and a programme of periodic reviews. The impact of the diagnosis on carers can be considered and addressed as well.

(c) More patients diagnosed will mean a greater strain on resources for care. Possibly some of this might be offset be providing more efficient and effective care than the patient might get without the right diagnosis.

(d) The intention is that the existence of the targets will prompt health professionals to be more alert than previously to whether an individual has dementia. Probably two of the important drivers of any improvement in diagnosis rates will be: the initial decision to consider dementia as an explanation for signs or symptoms, and the decision to refer the patient for further assessment. Exactly what this will involve will vary according to who first suspects dementia and what procedures and services are available.

References

Alzheimer's Disease International (2008) 'The prevalence of dementia worldwide' [online], http://www.alz.co.uk/adi/pdf/prevalence.pdf (Accessed November 2010).

APA (2000) *Diagnostic and Statistical Manual of Mental Disorders*, 4th edn, Text Revision (DSM-IV-TR).

Auld, D.S., Kornecook, T.J., Bastianetto, S. and Quirion, R. (2002) 'Alzheimer's disease and the basal forebrain cholinergic system: relations to β-amyloid peptides, cognition, and treatment strategies', *Progress in Neurobiology*, vol. 68, pp. 209–45.

Ballard, C. and Cream, J. (2005) 'Drugs used to relieve behavioural symptoms in people with dementia or an unacceptable chemical cosh? Argument', *International Psychogeriatrics*, vol. 17, no. 1, pp. 12–22.

Bamford, C. and Bruce, E. (2000) 'Defining the outcomes of community care: the perspectives of older people with dementia and their carers', *Ageing and Society*, vol. 20, pp. 543–70.

Banerjee, S. (2009) *The Use of Antipsychotic Medication for People with Dementia: Time for Action*, A report for the Minister of State for Care Services, Department of Health [online] http://www.dh.gov.uk/dr_consum_dh/groups/dh_digitalassets/ documents/digitalasset/dh_108302.pdf (Accessed September 2010).

Bell, R.D. and Zlokovic, B.V. (2009) 'Neurovascular mechanisms and blood–brain barrier disorder in Alzheimer's dementia', *Acta Neuropathologica*, vol. 118, pp. 103–13.

Bierer, L.M., Haroutunian, V., Gabriel, S., Knott, P.J., Carlin, L.S., Purohit, D.P. et al. (1995) 'Neurochemical correlates of dementia severity in Alzheimer's disease: relative importance of the cholinergic deficits', *Journal of Neurochemistry*, vol. 64, pp. 749–60.

Boustani, M., Sachs, G. and Callahan, C.M. (2007) 'Can primary care meet the biopsychosocial needs of older adults with dementia?', *Journal of General Internal Medicine*, vol. 22, no. 11, pp. 1625–7.

Brouwers, N., Sleegers, K. and Van Broeckhoven, C. (2008) 'Molecular genetics of Alzheimer's disease: an update', *Annals of Medicine*, vol. 40, pp. 562–83.

Cavalieri, M., Enzinger, C., Petrovic, K., Pluta-Fuerst, A., Homayoon, N., Schmidt, H. et al. (2010) 'Vascular dementia and Alzheimer's dementia – are we in a dead-end road?', *Neurodegenerative Diseases*, vol. 7, nos 1–3, pp. 122–6.

Chandra, V., Pandav, R., Dodge, H.H., Johnston, J.M., Belle, S.H., DeKosky, S.T. et al. (2001) 'Incidence of Alzheimer's disease in a rural community in India: the Indo-US study', *Neurology*, vol. 57, pp. 985–9.

Chenoweth, L., King, M.T., Jean, Y-H., Brodaty, H., Stein-Parbury, J., Norman, R. et al. (2009) 'Caring for Dementia Care Resident Study (CADRES) of person-centred care, dementia care mapping, and usual care in dementia: a cluster-randomised trial', *The Lancet*, vol. 8, pp. 317–25.

Cohen, D. and Eisdorfer, C. (1986) *The Loss of Self: A family resource for the care of Alzheimer's disease and related disorders*, London, W.W. Norton.

Cohen-Mansfield, J., Golander, H. and Arnheim, G. (2000) 'Self-identity in older persons suffering from dementia: preliminary results', *Social Science and Medicine*, vol. 51, pp. 381–94.

Cotrell, V. and Shultz, R. (1993) 'The perspective of the patient with Alzheimer's disease: a neglected dimension of dementia research', *The Gerontologist*, vol. 33, no. 2, pp. 205–11.

Cuddy, L.L. and Duffy, J. (2005) 'Music, memory and Alzheimer's disease: is music recognition spared in dementia, and how can it be assessed?' *Medical Hypotheses*, vol. 64, no. 2, pp. 229–35.

Datta, S. and Siwek, D.K. (1997) 'Excitation of brain stem pedunculopontine tegmentum cholinergic cells induces wakefulness and REM sleep', *Journal of Neurophysiology*, vol. 77, no. 6, pp. 2975–88.

Davis, K.L. (2008) 'Current and experimental therapeutics for Alzheimer's disease', Section 9, Chapter 87 in *Neuropsychopharmacology – 5th Generation of Progress*, American College of Neuropsychopharmacology [online], http://www.acnp.org/publications/neuro5thgeneration.aspx (Accessed September 2010).

de la Torre, J.C. (2009) 'Cerebrovascular and cardiovascular pathology in Alzheimer's dementia', *International Review of Neurobiology*, vol. 84, pp. 35–48.

Dening, T. (2009) 'Prescribing policy with dementia drugs: The UK Nice experience', *Maturitas*, vol. 64, pp. 59–60.

Dineley, K.T. (2007) 'Beta-amyloid peptide – nicotinic acetylcholine receptor interaction: the two faces of health and disease', *Frontiers in Bioscience*, vol. 12, pp. 5030–8.

Douglas, I.J. and Smeeth, L. (2009) 'Exposure to antipsychotics and risk of stroke: self controlled case series study', *British Medical Journal*, doi: 10.1136/bmj.a1227.

Dubois, B., Feldman, H.H., Jacova C., Dekosky, S.T., Barberger-Gateau, P., Cummings, J. et al. (2007) 'Research criteria for the diagnosis of Alzheimer's disease: revising the NINCDS–ADRDA criteria', *The Lancet Neurology*, vol. 6, pp. 734–46.

Edwards, P. (2010) *Introduction to Dementia Care Mapping* [online], vimeo.com/8040980 (Accessed September 2010).

Eikelenboom, P., Veerhuis, R., Scheper, W., Rozemuller, A.J.M., van Gool, W.A. and Hoozemans, J.J.M. (2006) 'The significance of neuroinflammation in understanding Alzheimer's disease', *Journal of Neural Transmission*, vol. 113, pp. 1685–95.

Ertekin-Taner, N. (2007) 'Genetics of Alzheimer's disease: a centennial review', *Neurologic Clinics*, vol. 25, pp. 611–17.

European Alzheimer's Disease Consortium (2010) [online] http://eadc.alzheimer-europe.org (Accessed November 2010).

Ferri, C.P., Prince, M., Brayne, C., Brodaty, H., Fratiglioni, L., Ganguli, M. et al. (2005) 'Global prevalence of dementia: a Delphi consensus study', *Lancet*, vol. 366, pp. 2112–7.

Folstein, M.F., Folstein, S.E. and McHugh, P.R. (1975) '"Mini-mental state". A practical method for grading the cognitive state of patients for the clinician', *Journal of Psychiatric Research*, vol. 12, no. 3, pp. 189–98.

Fox, P.J. (2000) 'The role of the concept of Alzheimer's disease in the development of the Alzheimer's Association in the United States', in Whitehouse, P.J., Maurer, K. and Ballenger, J.F. (eds) *Concepts of Alzheimer's Disease: Biological, Clinical and Cultural Perspectives*, Baltimore MD: Johns Hopkins University Press, pp. 209–33.

Ganguli, M., Dodge, H.H., Shen, C. and DeKosky, S.T. (2004) 'Mild cognitive impairment, amnestic type: an epidemiological study', *Neurology*, vol. 63, pp. 115–21.

Gibson, G., Timlin, A., Curran, S. and Watts, J. (2004) 'The scope for qualitative methods in research and clinical trials in dementia', *Age and Ageing*, vol. 33, pp. 422–6.

Gill, S.S., Rochon, P.A., Herrmann, M., Lee, P.E., Sykora, K., Gunraj, N. et al. (2005) 'Atypical antipsychotic drugs and risk of ischaemic stroke: population based retrospective cohort study', *British Medical Journal*, doi: 10.1136/bmj.38330.470486.8F.

Gladstone Institutes (2010) www.gladstone.ucsf.edu/gladstone/files/publicaffairs/mono3fig1.gif

Golomb, J., Kluger, A. and Ferris, S.H. (2004) 'Mild cognitive impairment: historical development and summary of research', *Dialogues in Clinical Neuroscience*, vol. 6, pp. 351–67.

Gormley, N., Lyons, D. and Howard, R. (2001) 'Behavioural management of aggression in dementia: a randomised controlled trial', *Age and Ageing*, vol. 30, pp. 141–5.

Gould, N. and Kendall, T. (2007) 'Developing the NICE/SCIE guidelines for dementia care: the challenges of enhancing the evidence base for social and health care', *British Journal of Social Work*, vol. 37, pp. 475–90.

Haass, C. and Selkoe, D.J. (2007) 'Soluble protein oligomers in neurodegeneration: lessons from the Alzheimer's amyloid β-peptide', *Nature Reviews Molecular Cell Biology*, vol. 8, pp. 101–2.

HealthCentral OurAlzheimer's.com (2008) [online], http://www.healthcentral.com/alzheimers/c/82723/26891/alzheimer (Accessed September 2010).

Henderson, A.S. and Jorm, A.F. (2002) 'Definition and epidemiology of dementia: a review', in Maj, M. and Sartorius, N. (eds) *Dementia* (2nd edn), WPA Series in Evidence and Experience in Psychiatry (Vol. 3), Chichester, John Wiley and Sons.

Hendrie, H.C., Ogunniyi, A., Hall, K.S., Baiyewu, O., Unverzagt, F.W., Gureje, O. et al. (2001) 'Incidence of dementia and Alzheimer disease in 2 communities: Yoruba residing in Ibadan, Nigeria, and African Americans residing in Indianapolis, Indiana', *Journal of the American Medical Association*, vol. 285, pp.739–47.

Hock, C., Konietzo, U., Streffer, J.R., Tracy, J., Signorell, A., Muller-Tillmanns, B. et al. (2003) 'Antibodies against β-amyloid slow cognitive decline in Alzheimer's disease', *Neuron*, vol. 38, pp. 547–54.

Hoffman, J. and Froemke, S. (2009) *The Alzheimer's Project: Momentum in Science*, New York, PublicAffairs, Perseus Books Group.

Innes, A. (2003) 'Dementia care mapping for care planning purposes', in Innes, A. (ed.) *Dementia Care Mapping: Applications Across Cultures*, Baltimore MD, Health Professions Press, pp. 71–80.

Innes, A. (2009) *Dementia Studies*, London, SAGE Publications Ltd.

Jedrziewski, M.K., Lee, V.M.-Y. and Trojanowski, J.Q. (2005) 'Lowering the risk of Alzheimer's disease: evidence-based practices emerge from new research', *Alzheimer's & Dementia*, vol. 1, pp. 152–60.

Kitwood, T. (1993) 'Person and process in dementia', *International Journal of Geriatric Psychiatry*, vol. 8, pp. 541–5.

Kitwood, T. and Bredin, K. (1992) 'A new approach to the evaluation of dementia care', *Journal of Advances in Health and Nursing Care*, vol. 1, no. 5, pp. 41–60.

Klein, W.L. (2006) 'Synaptic targeting by Aβ oligomers (ADDLS) as a basis for memory loss in early Alzheimer's disease', *Alzheimer's & Dementia*, vol. 2, pp. 43–55.

Kumar, A.M., Tims, F., Cruess, D.G., Mintzer, M.J., Ironson, G., Loewenstein, D. et al. (1999) 'Music therapy increases serum melatonin levels in patients with Alzheimer's disease', *Alternative Therapies in Health and Medicine*, vol. 5, no. 6, pp. 49–57.

Lee, H., Perry, G., Moreira, P.I., Garrett, M.R., Liu, Q., Zhu, X. et al. (2005) 'Tau phosphorylation in Alzheimer's disease: pathogen or protector?' *Trends in Molecular Medicine*, vol. 11, pp. 164–9.

Li, N-C., Lee, A., Whitmer, R.A., Kivipelto, M., Lawler, E., Kazis, L.E. and Wolozin, B. (2010) 'Use of angiotensin receptor blockers and risk of dementia in a predominantly male population: prospective cohort analysis', *British Medical Journal*, doi: 10.1136/bmj.b5465.

Lichtenthaler, S.F. and Haass, C. (2004) 'Amyloid at the cutting edge: activation of α-secretase prevents amyloidogenesis in an Alzheimer's disease mouse model', *Journal of Clinical Investigation*, vol. 113, pp. 1384–7.

Lobo A., Launer, L.J., Fratiglioni, L., Andersen, K., Di Carlo, A. and Breteler, M.M., Neurologic Diseases in the Elderly Research Group (2000) 'Prevalence of dementia and major subtypes in Europe: A collaborative study of population-based cohorts,' *Neurology*, vol. 54 (suppl. 5), pp. S4–S9.

Lyman, K.A. (1989) 'Bringing the social back in: a critique of the biomedicalization of dementia', *The Gerontologist*, vol. 29, no. 5, pp. 597–604.

MacKinnon, A., Christensen, H., Hofer, S.M., Korten, A.E. and Jorm, A.F. (2003) 'Use it and still lose it? The association between activity and cognitive performance established using latent growth sample techniques in a community sample', *Aging, Neuropsychology and Cognition*, vol. 10, no. 3, pp. 215–29.

Mathis, C.A., Klunk, W.E., Price, J.C. and DeKosky, S.T. (2005) 'Imaging technology for neurodegenerative diseases' *Archives of Neurology*, vol. 62, pp. 196–200.

McGeer, P.L. and McGeer, E.G. (2007) 'NSAIDs and Alzheimer disease: epidemiological, animal model and clinical studies', *Neurobiology of Aging*, vol. 28, pp. 639–47.

Medical Research Council Neuropathology Group (2001) Cognitive Function and Aging Study: 'Pathological correlates of late-onset dementia in a multicentre, community-based population in England and Wales', *The Lancet*, vol. 357, pp. 169–75.

Mitchell, A.J. and Shiri-Feshki, M. (2009) 'Rate of progression of mild cognitive impairment to dementia – meta-analysis of 41 robust inception cohort studies', *Acta Psychiatrica Scandinavica*, vol. 119, pp. 252–65.

Molnar, F.J., Son-Hing, M.M. and Fergusson, D. (2009) Systematic review of measures of clinical significance employed in randomised controlled trials of drugs for dementia, *Journal of the American Geriatrics Society*, vol. 57, no. 3, pp. 536–46.

Morris, J.C. (1993) 'The Clinical Dementia Rating (CDR): current version and scoring rules', *Neurology*, vol. 43, pp. 2412–4.

Morris, R.G.M., Anderson, E., Lynch, G.S. and Baudry, M. (1986) 'Selective impairment of learning and blockade of long-term potentiation by an N-methyl-D-aspartate receptor antagonist, AP5', *Nature*, vol. 319, pp. 774–6.

Mucke, L. (2009) 'Alzheimer's disease', *Nature*, vol. 461, pp. 895–7.

NICE (National Institute for Health and Clinical Excellence) (2006) Quick Reference Guide: Clinical Guideline 42. *Dementia: Supporting People with Dementia and their Carers in Health and Social Care* [online], http://www.nice.org.uk/nicemedia/live/10998/30317/30317.pdf (Accessed September 2010).

Nilsson, L.G. (2003) 'Memory function in normal aging', *Acta Neurologica Scandinavica*, vol. 107 (suppl. 179), pp. 7–13.

NursingTimes.net (2006) *Dementia Care Mapping* [online] 19 September 2006, http://www.nursingtimes.net/nursing-practice-clinical-research/dementia-care-mapping/201154.article (Accessed September 2010).

O'Bryant, S.E., Humphreys, J.D., Smith, G.E., Ivnik, R.J., Graff-Radford, N.R., Petersen, R.C. and Lucas, J.A. (2008) 'Detecting dementia with the mini-mental state examination in highly educated individuals', *Archives of Neurology*, vol. 65, no. 7, pp. 963–7.

Oddo, S., Caccamo, A., Green, K.N., Liang, K., Tran, L., Chen, Y., Leslie, F.M. and LaFerla, F.M. (2005) 'Chronic nicotine administration exacerbates tau pathology in a transgenic model of Alzheimer's disease', *Proceedings of the National Academy of Sciences*, vol. 102, pp. 3046–51.

Oommen, G., Bashford, J. and Shah, A. (2009) 'Ageing, ethnicity and psychiatric services', *Psychiatric Bulletin*, vol. 33, pp. 30–4.

Paran, E., Anson, O. and Lowenthal, D.T. (2010) 'Cognitive function and antihypertensive treatment in the elderly: a 6-year follow-up study', *American Journal of Therapeutics*, vol. 17, no. 4, pp. 358–64.

Perez, C.A. and Cancela Carral, J.M. (2008) 'Benefits of physical exercise for older adults with Alzheimer's disease', *Geriatric Nursing*, vol. 29, no. 6, pp. 384–91.

Perry, E.K. (1986) 'The cholinergic hypothesis – ten years on', *British Medical Bulletin*, vol. 42, pp. 63–9.

Petersen, R.C., Smith, G.E., Waring, S.C., Ivnik, R.J., Tangalos, E.G. and Kokmen, E. (1999) 'Mild cognitive impairment: clinical characterization and outcome', *Archives of Neurology*, vol. 56, pp. 303–8.

PhRMA (2009) Medicines in Development for Women [online], http://www.phrma.org/medicines_in_development_for_women (Accessed September 2010).

Prins, N.D., Visser, P.J. and Scheltens, P. (2010) 'Can novel therapeutics halt the amyloid cascade?' *Alzheimer's Research & Therapy*, 2:28 [online], http://alzres.com/content/pdf/alzrt28.pdf (Accessed September 2010).

Qaseem, A., Snow, V., Cross, J., Forclea, M.A., Hopkins Jr, R., Shekelle P. et al. and the Joint American College of Physicians/American Academy of Family Physicians Panel on Dementia (2008) 'Current pharmacologic treatment of dementia: a clinical practice guideline from the American College of Physicians and the American Academy of Family Physicians', *Annals of Internal Medicine*, vol. 148, pp. 370–8.

Rafii, M.S. and Aisen, P.S. (2009) 'Recent developments in Alzheimer's disease therapeutics', *BMC Medicine*, 7:7 [online], http://www.biomedcentral.com/content/pdf/1741-7015-7-7.pdf (Accessed September 2010).

Ralna, P., Santaguida, P., Ismaila, A., Patterson, C., Cowan, D., Levine, M. et al. (2008) 'Effectiveness of cholinesterase inhibitors and memantine for treating dementia: evidence review for a clinical practice guideline', *Annals of Internal Medicine*, vol. 148, pp. 379–97.

Reisberg, B., Doody, R., Stoffler, A., Schmitt, F., Ferris, S. and Mobius, H-J. (2003) 'Memantine in moderate-to-severe Alzheimer's disease', *New England Journal of Medicine*, vol. 348, no. 14, pp. 1333–41.

Rinne, J.O., Brooks, D.J., Rossor, M.N., Fox, N.C., Bullock, R., Klunk, W.E. et al. (2010) '11C-PiB PET assessment of change in fibrillar amyloid-beta load in patients with Alzheimer's disease treated with bapineuzumab: a phase 2, double-blind, placebo-controlled, ascending-dose study', *The Lancet Neurology*, vol. 9, no. 4, pp. 363–72.

Ritchie, K. (2004) 'Mild cognitive impairment: an epidemiological perspective', *Dialogues in Clinical Neuroscience*, vol. 6, pp. 401–8.

Rubio, A., Perez, M. and Avila, J. (2006) 'Acetylcholine receptors and tau phosphorylation', *Current Molecular Medicine*, vol. 6, pp. 423–8.

Sadowsky, C.H., Farlow, M.R., Meng, X. and Olin, J.T. (2010) 'Safety and tolerability of rivastigmine transdermal patch compared with rivastigmine capsules in patients switched from donepezil: data from three clinical trials', *The International Journal of Clinical Practice*, vol. 64, no. 2, pp. 188–93.

Salmon, D. and Hodges, J.R. (2005) 'Mild cognitive impairment – cognitive, behavioral, and biological factors', *Neurocase*, vol. 11, no. 1, pp. 1–2.

Schenk, D., Barbour, R., Dunn, W., Gordon, G., Grajeda, H., Guido, T. et al. (1999) 'Immunization with amyloid-β attenuates Alzheimer-disease-like pathology in the PDAPP mouse', *Nature*, vol. 400, pp. 173–7.

Schliebs, R. and Arendt, T. (2006) 'The significance of the cholinergic system in the brain during ageing and in Alzheimer's disease', *Journal of Neural Transmission*, vol. 113, pp. 1625–44.

Schneider, P., Hampel, H. and Buerger, K. (2009) 'Biological marker candidates of Alzheimer's dementia in blood, plasma and serum', *CNS Neuroscience & Therapeutics*, vol. 15, no. 4, pp. 358–74.

Schuff, N., Woerner, N., Boreta, L., Kornfield, T., Shaw, L.M., Trojanowski, J.Q. et al. (2009) 'MRI of hippocampal volume loss in early Alzheimer's disease in relation to ApoE genotype and biomarkers', *Brain*, vol. 132, pp. 1067–77.

Selkoe, D.J. (1994) 'Alzheimer's disease: a central role for amyloid', *Journal of Neuropathology and Experimental Neurology*, vol. 53, pp. 438–47.

Seltzer, B., Zolnouni, P., Nunez, M., Goldman, R., Kumar, D., Ieni, J. and Richardson, S. (2004) 'Efficacy of donepezil in early-stage Alzheimer disease: a randomized placebo-controlled trial', *Archives of Neurology*, vol. 61, pp. 1852–6.

Shah, R.S., Lee, H.-G., Xiongwei, Z., Perry, G., Smith, M.A. and Castellani, R.J. (2008) 'Current approaches in the treatment of Alzheimer's disease', *Biomedicine & Pharmacotherapy*, vol. 62, no. 4, pp. 199–207.

Shankar, G.M. and Walsh, D.M. (2009) 'Alzheimer's disease: synaptic dysfunction and Aβ', *Molecular Neurodegeneration*, vol. 4: 48, doi: 10.1186/1750-1326-4-48.

Snowdon, D.A., Greiner, L.H., Mortimer, J.A., Riley, K.P., Greiner, P.A. and Markesbery, W.R. (1997) 'Brain infarction and the clinical expression of Alzheimer disease. The Nun Study', *Journal of the American Medical Association*, vol. 277, pp. 813–17.

Spector, A. (2006) 'A review of the use of cognitive stimulation therapy in dementia management', *British Journal of Neuroscience Nursing*, vol. 2, no. 8, pp. 381–5.

Spector, A., Thorgrimsen, L., Woods, B., Royan, L., Davies, S., Butterworth, M. and Orrell, M. (2006) 'Efficacy of an evidence-based cognitive stimulation therapy programme for people with dementia: randomised control trial', *British Journal of Psychiatry*, vol. 183, pp. 248–54.

Sperling, R.A., Bates, J.F. and Chua, E.F. (2003) 'fMRI studies of associative encoding in young and elderly controls and mild Alzheimer's disease', *Journal of Neurology, Neurosurgery & Psychiatry*, vol. 74, pp. 44–50.

Sperlinger, D., Clare, L., Bradbury, N. and Culverwell, A. (2004) 'Measuring outcome in routine clinical practice: Paper 3,' *Measuring Psychosocial Treatment Outcomes with Older People*, The British Psychological Society.

Tanzi, R. (2005) 'The synaptic Aβ hypothesis of Alzheimer disease', *Nature Neuroscience*, vol. 8, pp. 977–9.

UK Alzheimer's Society (2007) Personal Social Services Research Unit, Institute of Psychiatry, *Dementia UK: The Full Report*, London, Alzheimer's Society.

UK Alzheimer's Society (2010) [online], www.alzheimers.org.uk (Accessed September 2010).

UK Department of Health (2009) *Living Well with Dementia: A National Dementia Strategy*.

UK Office for National Statistics (2010) UK National Statistics [online], www.statistics.gov.uk/hub/population/index.html (Accessed November 2010).

University of Bradford/BSI (2010) *PAS 800: Use of Dementia Care Mapping for Improved Person-Centred Care in a Care Provider Organization – Guide*.

Valenzuela, M. and Sachdev, P. (2009) 'Can cognitive exercise prevent the onset of dementia? Systematic review of randomised clinical trials with longitudinal follow-up', *American Journal of Geriatric Psychiatry*, vol. 17, no. 3, pp. 179–87.

Vink, A.C., Birks, J., Bruinsma, M.S. and Scholtens, R.J.P.M. (2003) 'Music therapy for people with dementia', *Cochrane Database of Systematic Reviews 2003*, issue 4. art. no. CD003477.

Wang, T. and Tang, X.C. (1998) 'Reversal of scopolamine-induced deficits in radial maze performance by (-)-huperzine A: comparison with E2020 and tacrine', *European Journal of Pharmacology*, vol. 349, pp. 137–42.

Whalley, L.J., Deary, I.J., Appleton, C.L. and Starr, J.M. (2004) 'Cognitive reserve and the neurobiology of aging', *Ageing Research Reviews*, vol. 3, pp. 369–82.

WHO (1994) *The International Statistical Classification of Diseases and Related Health Problems*, 10th revision (ICD-10).

Woods, R., Spector, A., Jones, C., Orrell, M. and Davies, S. (2005) 'Reminiscence therapy for dementia: a review of the evidence of effectiveness from randomised controlled trails', *Cochrane Database of Systematic Reviews 2005*, issue 2, art. no. CD001120 (edited 2009).

Acknowledgements

Grateful acknowledgement is made to Christine Heading for contributions to Sections 2.7, 2.8 and 4.10 and to Katherine Leys for coordinating the Research Methods boxes throughout SDK228.

Grateful acknowledgement is also made to the following sources:

Text

Box 3.4: Ballard C. and Cream J. (2005) 'Should novel antipsychotics ever be used to treat the behavioral and psychological symptoms of dementia (BPSD)?', *International Psychogeriatric*, vol. 17, no. 1, International Psychogeriatric Association.

Tables

Table 4.3: Spector, A. and Orrell, M. (2006) 'A review of the use of cognitive stimulation therapy in dementia management', *British Journal of Neuroscience Nursing*, vol. 2, no 8. MA Healthcare.

Figures

Figure 1.1: Christopher Nash/Alamy; Figures 1.2, 1.3, 1.4 and 3.5: Courtesy Google Inc; Figure 1.5: Corking, S. (2002) 'What's new with the amnesic patient H.M.?', *Nature Reviews-Neuroscience*, vol. 13, Feb 2002. Macmillan Magazines Limited; Figure 1.7: Alzheimer Scotland – Action on Dementia; Figures 1.8 and 2.4: Copyright © 2008–2010 Elements4Health; Figure 1.9: Copyright © 2010 PAR, Inc. All rights reserved; Figure 1.10: John Livzey/ Getty Images; Figure 1.11: Reisberg, B. (1988) 'Functional Assessment Staging (FAST)', *Psychopharmacology Bulletin*, vol. 24, pp. 653–659. Copyright © 1984 by Barry Reisber, M.D. Reproduced with permission; Figure 1.12: ontarioseniors.blogspot.com; Figure 1.13: Nilsson, L.G. (2003) 'Memory function in normal aging', *Acta Neurology Scandinavica*, 107, suppl 179. Wiley; Figure 1.15: Petersen, R. et al. (1999), 'Mild Cognitive Impairment – clinical characterisation and outcome', *Archives of Neurology*, vol. 59. American Medical Association; Figure 1.16: Mayo Foundation for Medical Education and Research; Figure 1.17: © 2010 Alzheimer's Association. All rights reserved; Figure 2.1: Agamanolis D., M.D. Akron Children's Hospital and Professor of Pathology (neuropathology) at Northeastern Ohio Universities College of Medicine; Figure 2.3: UCSF School of Medicine; Figure 2.5: Sperling, R.A., Bates J.F. Chua E.F. et al., (2010), 'fMRI studies of associative encoding in young and elderly controls and mild Alzheimer's disease', *Journal of Neurology*, vol. 74, *Neurosurgery & Psychiatry*, BMJ Publishing Group; Figure 2.6: www.sciencedaily.com; Figure 2.8: Bierer, L. M. (1995) 'Neurochemical correlates of dementia severity in Alzheimer's disease', *Journal of Neurochemistry*, vol. 64, Wiley; Figure 2.10: Wang, T. and Can Tang Xi (1998) 'Reversal of scopolamine-induced deficits in radial maze performance by (−) Huperzine A', *European Journal of Pharmacology*, vol. 349. Elsevier Science; Figure 3.2: Seltzer, B.

SDK228 Team

Claire Rostron (*SDK228 Chair and Academic Editor*)
Basiro Davey (*Advisor*)
Viki Burnage (*SDK228 Manager*)
Helen Copperwheat (*SDK228 Assistant*)
Frederick Toates (*Block 1 Chair*)
Antonio Martins-Mourao
Saroj Datta (*Block 2 Chair*)
Heather McLannahan (*SDK228 Deputy Chair*)
Ellie Dommett (*Block 3 Chair*)
Katherine Leys (*Block 4 Chair*)

Consultants

Ilona Boniwell
Christine Heading
Margaret Swithenby

External assessor

Professor Neil Frude

Critical readers

Meg Barker
Mick McCormick
Ulf Wagner

Developmental testers

Elena Gammage
Jen Evans
Vicky Gaeta

Production team

Greg Black
Ann Carter
Martin Chiverton
Roger Courthold
Rebecca Graham
Sara Hack
Nicky Heath
Chris Hough
Carol Houghton
Roger Moore
Jon Owen
Judith Pickering
Brian Richardson

Federica Sacco
Bina Sharma

Indexer

Jane Henley

Library

Duncan Belks

Index

Index terms and page numbers in **bold** refer to glossary terms. Page numbers in *italics* refer to terms in figures or tables

see also CDR (Clinical Dementia
Rating) Scale; Mini Mental
State Examination (MMSE)
SD (standard deviation) 27, 28
secondary dementias 5
secretases 56, *57,* 58, 93
inhibitors 62
seizures 9, 10
self-neglect 4, 32
SEM (standard error of the mean)
55, 86
semantic dementia 34
semantic memory 11, *12,* 13, 26,
27, 29
sense of self 117–18, 132
severe dementia *22*
Severe Impairment Battery 85, *86*
side effects
antipsychotics 87–8, 89
beta-amyloid vaccine 97
drugs 76, 78–9, 85, *92*
reminiscence therapy 118
significant difference *80, 86, 97,*
115, 123, 124
sleep patterns 121
smoking 37, 80–2
social behaviour 2, 16, 33
social construction 131–2
SPECAL 118–19
standard deviation (SD) 27, 28
standard error of the mean (SEM)
55, 86
statins 100
statistically significant 114–15, 124
stigma 15
stroke 37, 38, 88
subclinical 26, 29
subjective experience of dementia
108, 132
susceptibility genes 70, 71
synaptic dysfunction 61–2, *96*
synaptic plasticity 61, 62

T

t-test 114–15
tangles *see* **neurofibrillary tangles**
tarenflurbil 93
task-centred approach **110,** 111
tau protein **34**–5, 42, 62–5, *67*

in amyloid cascade *96*
potential drug treatments 94
and smoking 81
temporal cortex 9–11, *16,* 32, 43,
44
therapeutic group work 124–6
tissue cultures 59–60
tolerance, to drugs 78, *92*
**transdermal route of
administration 79**
transgenic 52, 69, 73, 97
treatment condition 113, *116, 123,*
139

U

UK Alzheimer's Society 66, *68,* 69
'Dementia UK: The Full Report'
126, *127*
UK Department of Health and
Social Care 127
US Genetic Information
Nondiscrimination Act (2008) 71
'use it or lose it' 130

V

vaccines 62, 97–8
validity 23
vascular 4, *67*
vascular dementia 4, 35–8
with AD 35
causes of 37
signs and symptoms 36
treatment, course and prognosis
38
vignette 4–5, 35–6
vascular disease, and AD 98–100
vascular system *35,* 37
Vignette 1.1 Experiences of
dementia: Martha and Saul 2
Vignette 1.2 Experiences of
dementia: Filip and Anna 3
Vignette 1.3 Frontotemporal and
vascular dementias 4–5
Vignette 1.4 Diagnosing
Alzheimer's dementia: Filip's case
19–20
Vignette 1.5 Differentiating
dementia and depresssion: Bill's
case 24

Vignette 1.6 Ageing and memory
loss: Norma's experience 25
Vignette 1.7 Caring for someone
with late-stage Alzheimer's
dementia: Anna's advice 31
Vignette 1.8 Frontotemporal
dementia: Sally's case 32–3
Vignette 1.9 Vascular dementia:
Joy's case as told by her daughter
35–6
Vignette 4.1 The impact of
dementia care mapping 108–9
Vignette 4.2 Losing oneself in
dementia 118
Vignette 4.3 The efficacy of music
therapy as reported by a music
therapist 120–1
visuospatial ability 85
voluntary carers 130

W–Z

wandering 5, 35
well-being 107, 109
working memory 11, 26, *27,* 29
errors 54, *55*
World Health Organization (WHO),
differential diagnosis guidelines
23–4
z-scores 27–8